GLENCOE SPANISH 1

Bienvenidos

Writing Activities Workbook
and
Student Tape Manual

Protase E. Woodford

Conrad J. Schmitt

Glencoe McGraw-Hill

New York, New York   Columbus, Ohio   Woodland Hills, California   Peoria, Illinois

Glencoe/McGraw-Hill

A Division of The **McGraw·Hill** *Companies*

Send all inquiries to:
Glencoe/McGraw-Hill
8787 Orion Place
Columbus, OH 43240

ISBN 0-02-641004-4 (Teacher's Annotated Edition, Writing Activities Workbook)
ISBN 0-02-641017-6 (Teacher's Edition, Student Tape Manual)
ISBN 0-02-641003-6 (Student Edition, Writing Activities Workbook and Student
                        Tape Manual)

Printed in the United States of America.

    19   009   04 03 02

Writing Activities Workbook
and
Student Tape Manual

WRITING ACTIVITIES WORKBOOK
CONTENIDO

CAPÍTULO 1

UN AMIGO
UNA AMIGA

VOCABULARIO

Palabras 1

A   **Un mexicano.** This is Francisco (Paco) Guzmán. The following information about him is wrong. Rewrite the sentences, giving the correct information about Paco.

Guadalajara

Paco Guzmán es un muchacho puertorriqueño. Él es de San Juan. Él es bajo. Es moreno. Paco es alumno en una escuela secundaria norteamericana.

_____

_____

_____

_____

B **Una colombiana.** María Bustamente is from Cartagena, Colombia. Complete the sentences by writing what you know about her.

1. María no es ecuatoriana. Ella es _____.

2. Ella no es de Guayaquil. Es de _____.

3. María no es baja. Es bastante _____.

4. Ella no es alumna en un colegio ecuatoriano. Ella es alumna en un _____ colombiano.

C **Lo contrario.** Match the word in the left column with its opposite in the right column.

1. _____ bajo   **a.** tímido
2. _____ rubio   **b.** no
3. _____ divertido   **c.** antipático
4. _____ simpático   **d.** moreno
5. _____ sí   **e.** alto

D **Pablo Smith. ¿Cómo es?** Here is a picture of Pablo Smith. Describe him.

_____

_____

_____

_____

_____

E **Natalia Casals. ¿Cómo es?** Here is a picture of Natalia Casals. Describe her.

_____

_____

_____

_____

_____

Palabras 2

F **Yo.** Write as much about yourself as you can.

1. Hola. Yo soy _____

2. Soy de _____

3. Soy _____

4. _____

5. _____

G **Una pregunta.** Complete with a question word.

1. Roberto es de California.

    ¿_____ es de California?

2. Roberto es de California.

    ¿De _____ es Roberto?

3. Roberto es alto y moreno.

    ¿_____ es Roberto?

4. Roberto es americano.

    ¿De _____ nacionalidad es Roberto?

5. Roberto es amigo de Bárbara.

    ¿De _____ es amigo Roberto?

H **Juanita Torres.** This is Juanita Torres.
She is from Guayaquil, Ecuador.
Write four questions about her.

1. _____

2. _____

3. _____

4. _____

ESTRUCTURA

Los artículos definidos e indefinidos
Formas singulares

A **Pero, ¿quién es?** Complete the cartoon with *el* or *la*.

B **Un instituto educativo.** Complete with *un* or *una*.

1. _____ instituto es _____ escuela.

2. _____ academia es _____ escuela.

3. _____ colegio es _____ escuela también.

4. Roberto es _____ alumno en _____ escuela secundaria americana.

5. María es _____ alumna en _____ colegio en Cali, Colombia.

6. María es _____ persona muy sincera.

7. Roberto es _____ muchacho honesto.

La concordancia de los adjetivos
Formas singulares

C ¿Quién es? Describe the boy.

_____

_____

_____

D ¿Quién es? Describe the girl.

_____

_____

_____

_____

El presente del verbo ser
Formas singulares

E Yo. Answer about yourself.

1. ¿Quién eres?

_____

2. ¿De dónde eres?

_____

3. ¿De qué nacionalidad eres?

_____

4. ¿Dónde eres alumno(a)?

_____

5. ¿Cómo eres?

_____

6. ¿De quién eres amigo(a)?

_____

F **Y tú.** This is Gloria. Tell her
what you think about her.

1. Gloria, eres _____

2. _____

3. _____

4. _____

G **Una tarjeta.** Read the following postcard from Clarita Buñuelos.

Yo soy Clarita Buñuelos.
Yo soy de La Paz, Bolivia.
Soy boliviana. Soy alumna
en una academia privada
para muchachas. Soy
una persona sincera y
honesta. Y soy seria.
pero de ninguna manera
soy aburrida.
Clarita

H **Clarita.** Write some things Clarita says about herself in her postcard.

_____

_____

_____

I   **Yo.** Now write a postcard to Clarita. Tell her all about yourself.

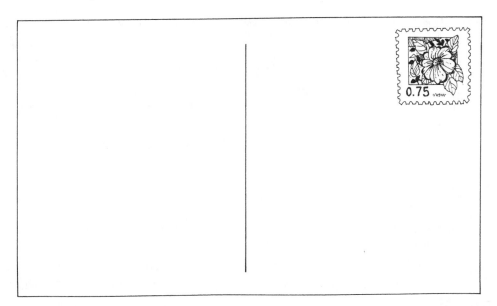

J   **¿Quién eres?** A young man has just walked up to you on the street. He thinks he recognizes you, but you are not sure who he is. Complete the conversation you are having with this person.

MUCHACHO: Hola, ¿qué tal?

TÚ: Muy bien, gracias. ¿Y tú?

MUCHACHO: Muy bien, gracias. Tú _____ _____ (your name).
                                                1   2

TÚ: Sí, _____ _____ (your name).
                       3   4

MUCHACHO: Tú _____ el/la amigo(a) de Teresa Salas, ¿no?
                             5

TÚ: Sí, yo _____ un(a) amigo(a) de Teresa Salas. Pero, perdón.
                          6

   ¿Quién _____ tú?
                   7

MUCHACHO: Yo _____ Roberto. Roberto Jones.
                    8

TÚ: Ay, sí. Perdón, Roberto. Tú _____ el amigo norteamericano de
                                            9

   Teresa, ¿verdad? Tú _____ de Miami, ¿no?
                              10

MUCHACHO: Sí, yo _____ de Miami. Tú _____ de Cali, ¿no?
                         11   12

TÚ: Sí, yo _____ de Cali y yo _____ amigo(a) de Teresa
                     13   14

   también. Ella _____ muy simpática, ¿no?
                         15

MUCHACHO: Sí, es una amiga muy sincera y _____ muy divertida también.
                                       16

UN POCO MÁS

A **La nacionalidad.** Tell what nationality a person from each of the following cities is.

1. _____ 2. _____ 3. _____

B **Más informes.** Every chapter in your workbook will include readings. These readings have unfamiliar words in them, but you should be able to understand them rather easily. You have probably noticed that many Spanish words look a lot like English words. So when you do not know the meaning of a word, take a guess. Try to understand the following reading.

Teresa Tamayo es una muchacha mexicana. Ella es de la capital, la Ciudad de México. La Ciudad de México es una ciudad grande, con una población de casi 20 millones de habitantes. Es realmente enorme.

Teresa es alumna en un colegio privado para muchachas en Lomas de Chapultepec. Lomas de Chapultepec es una colonia (una zona, un barrio) elegante de la Ciudad de México. "Tamayo" es un nombre famoso en México. Es el nombre de un pintor (artista), Rufino Tamayo.

C **El nombre Tamayo.** Tell whether each statement is true or false.

1. _____ Teresa Tamayo lives in a city near the capital of her country.
2. _____ She attends a coeducational school.
3. _____ Mexico City is an extremely large city.
4. _____ The name "Tamayo" is quite famous in Mexico.

D **Un nombre famoso.** Explain why the name "Tamayo" is famous in Mexico.

_____

_____

E **Palabras afines.** Find the Spanish words for the following in the reading selection.

1. population _____
2. inhabitants _____
3. enormous _____
4. section of a city _____
5. famous _____

MI AUTOBIOGRAFÍA

Begin to write your autobiography in Spanish. You will have fun adding to it as you continue with your study of Spanish. To begin, tell who you are and where you are from. Indicate your nationality and tell where you are a student. Also, give a brief description of yourself. What do you look like? How would you describe your personality?

mi autobiografía

CAPÍTULO

2

¿HERMANOS O AMIGOS?

VOCABULARIO

Palabras 1

A **Lo contrario.** Match the word in the left column with its opposite in the right column.

1. _____ pequeño   **a.** aburrido
2. _____ inteligente   **b.** el alumno
3. _____ interesante   **c.** grande
4. _____ amable   **d.** difícil
5. _____ fácil   **e.** estúpido
6. _____ el profesor   **f.** antipático

B **Una pregunta.** Choose the correct question word.

1. *Ella* es Lupita.
   a. Cómo
   b. De dónde
   c. Quién

2. Lupita es *chilena.*
   a. Cómo
   b. Quién
   c. Qué

3. Ella es *alumna.*
   a. Cómo
   b. Qué
   c. Dónde

4. La profesora es *interesante.*
   a. Cómo
   b. Qué
   c. Dónde

5. Ella es de *Santiago, la capital.*
   a. De dónde
   b. Qué
   c. Quién

6. *Lupita y Teresa* son amigas.
   a. Quién
   b. Quiénes
   c. Cómo

7. Las dos son *muy divertidas.*
   a. Quiénes
   b. Qué
   c. Cómo

8. Los alumnos son *hermanos.*
   a. Quiénes
   b. Qué
   c. Cómo

Palabras 2

C ¿Qué son? Complete each sentence with an appropriate word.

1. La biología, la química y la física son _____.

2. El inglés, el español, el chino y el ruso son _____.

3. El latín es una _____ antigua.

4. El francés y el español son _____ modernas.

5. La _____, la geografía y la sociología son ciencias sociales.

6. La zoología y la botánica son partes de la _____.

7. El fútbol, el vólibol y el básquetbol son _____.

8. El álgebra, la geometría y la trigonometría son partes de las _____.

D Alumnos, profesores y cursos. Tell whether each statement is true or false.

1. _____ Los alumnos serios son estudiosos.

2. _____ Los alumnos buenos no son estudiosos.

3. _____ Los profesores interesantes son aburridos.

4. _____ Los profesores aburridos son buenos.

5. _____ Los profesores simpáticos son populares con los alumnos.

6. _____ Los cursos interesantes son populares con los alumnos.

7. _____ Los cursos difíciles y aburridos son populares con los alumnos.

E Los cursos. Write the names of all the courses you are taking this year.

_____

_____

_____

F ¿Cómo son los cursos? Rate your courses using the following words.

  difícil   fácil   aburrido   interesante   divertido

_____

_____

_____

_____

ESTRUCTURA

Los sustantivos, artículos y adjetivos
Formas plurales

A **Son Maripaz y Linda.** Maripaz and Linda are from Bogotá. Write four sentences about them.

1. _____
2. _____
3. _____
4. _____

B **Son Tomás y Felipe.** Tomás and Felipe are from Bogotá. Write four sentences about them.

1. _____
2. _____
3. _____
4. _____

C **El plural, por favor.** Rewrite each sentence in the plural.

1. El muchacho es inteligente y serio.

   _____

2. La muchacha es inteligente y divertida.

   _____

3. El muchacho es el hermano de Inés.

   _____

4. El curso interesante es popular.

   _____

5. El profesor inteligente es interesante.

   _____

6. La clase es grande.

   _____

7. El curso es interesante pero bastante difícil.

   _____

El presente del verbo ser
Formas plurales

D **Una carta.** Complete the following letter in which you talk about yourself and your brother. Pretend your brother is Carlos.

Carlos y yo _____ hermanos.
Nosotros _____ americanos.
_____ alumnos en una
escuela secundaria. _____
alumnos en la Escuela _____.

E **Amigos nuevos.** You have just met two new friends, Anita and Manolo. Ask them if they are the following.

1. hermanos

_____

2. amigos

_____

3. alumnos

_____

4. mexicanos

_____

F **El hermano de Ángela.** Complete the conversation.

Hola, Teresa. ¿Quién _____ el muchacho?

_____ Tomás. Él _____ el hermano de Ángela.

Ah, ¿él y Ángela _____ hermanos?

Sí, y _____ alumnos en la Escuela Nacional.

Tú también _____ alumna en la Escuela Nacional, ¿no?

Sí, nosotros tres _____ alumnos en la misma escuela.

¿_____ Uds. amigos?

Sí, _____ muy buenos amigos.

La hora

G **¿Qué hora es?** Write sentences telling the time on each of the clocks.

1. _____

2. _____

3. _____

4. _____

5. _____

6. _____

7. _____

8. _____

UN POCO MÁS

A **El zodíaco.** Read the characteristics for each sign of the zodiac.

HORÓSCOPO

Capricornio
22 diciembre–19 enero
eficiente, perseverante

Acuario
20 enero–18 febrero
sereno, ingenioso

Piscis
19 febrero–20 marzo
imaginativo, creativo

Aries
21 marzo–19 abril
aventurero, valiente

Tauro
20 abril–20 mayo
persistente, práctico

Géminis
21 mayo–21 junio
generoso, diligente

Cáncer
22 junio–22 julio
simpático, leal

Leo
23 julio–22 agosto
liberal, riguroso

Virgo
23 agosto–22 septiembre
lógico, sistemático

Libra
24 septiembre–23 octubre
artístico, sensitivo

Escorpión
24 octubre–21 noviembre
social, elocuente

Sagitario
22 noviembre–21 diciembre
independiente, bueno

B **Los amigos.** Name some friends and complete.

1. El signo de _____ es _____. Él/Ella es muy
   _____.

2. El signo de _____ y _____ es _____.
   Ellos / Ellas son muy _____.

C **El zodíaco.** Give your zodiac sign and describe yourself. Give as many characteristics of yourself as you can.

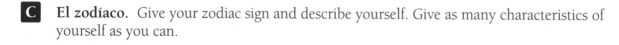

_____

_____

_____

D **Un poco de geografía.** Read the following. Take an educated guess at words you do not know.

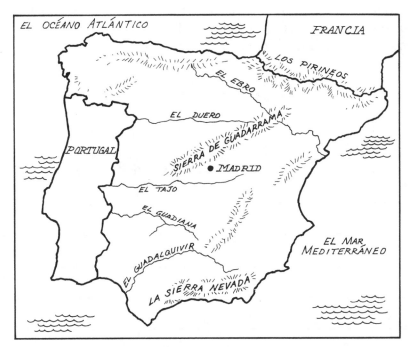

España es un país. La capital de España es Madrid. Madrid es una ciudad muy bonita. Los Pirineos forman la frontera entre España y Francia. Otras montañas de España son la Sierra de Guadarrama y la Sierra Nevada.

Los ríos importantes de España son el Duero, el Guadalquivir, el Guadiana, el Tajo y el Ebro.

E **Las fronteras.** Look at the map in Exercise D. Then circle the names of the places that border on Spain.

Italia	los Pirineos
Francia	el mar Caribe
Grecia	el océano Atlántico
Portugal	el océano Pacífico
los Andes	el mar Mediterráneo

F **La geografía de los Estados Unidos.** Tell what each of the following is.

1. el Misisipí _____

2. el Pacífico _____

3. las Rocosas _____

4. Wáshington, D.C. _____

MI AUTOBIOGRAFÍA

Continue with your autobiography. Write a list of the courses you are taking now. Tell who the teacher of each course is. Describe each course. Is it interesting, boring, easy, or difficult? Then tell something about your school friends. What are they like? What is their nationality?

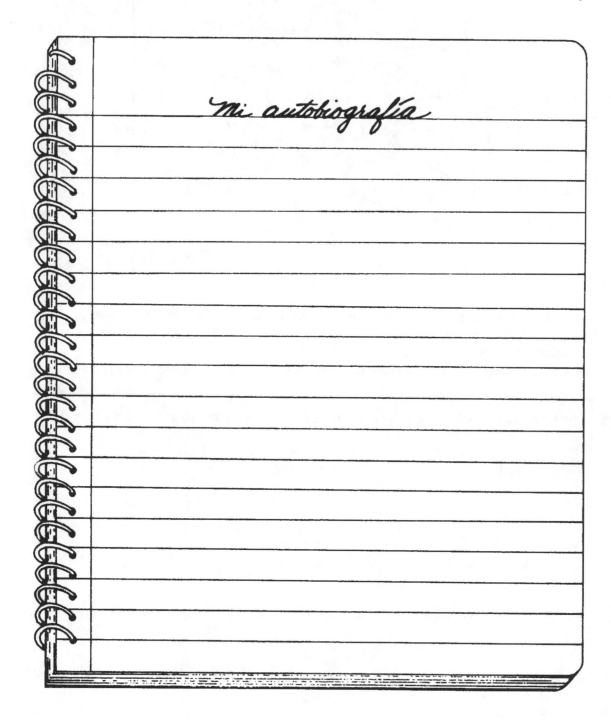

CAPÍTULO

3

EN LA ESCUELA

VOCABULARIO

Palabras 1

A **¿Qué es?** Write the name of each item.

1. _____ 2. _____ 3. _____

4. _____ 5. _____

B **En la escuela.** Answer the questions according to the illustrations.

1. ¿A qué hora llega José a la escuela?

_____

_____

¿Cómo llega?

_____

_____

2. ¿Con quién habla la alumna?

_____

_____

¿Dónde habla con la profesora?

_____

_____

3. ¿Qué lleva la muchacha?

_____

_____

¿En qué lleva los libros?

_____

_____

Palabras 2

C **¿El alumno o el profesor?** Complete each sentence with the appropriate word(s).

1. En una escuela americana "A" es una nota _____ y "F" es una nota

_____.

2. El profesor _____; el alumno _____ la pizarra.

3. El alumno _____ un examen y _____ una nota buena

en el _____.

4. El alumno _____ la lección en el libro (manual) escolar.

5. El profesor habla y el alumno toma _____ en un _____.

D **Palabras derivadas.** Many of the verbs you have learned have related nouns. Match each verb in the left column with the corresponding noun in the right column.

1. _____ entrar   **a.** la toma
2. _____ llegar   **b.** el examen
3. _____ tomar   **c.** la entrada
4. _____ estudiar   **d.** la mirada
5. _____ examinar   **e.** el estudio
6. _____ enseñar   **f.** la llegada
7. _____ mirar   **g.** la enseñanza

E **Un sinónimo.** Match the word in the left column with a word or expression that means the same in the right column.

1. _____ la nota   **a.** el pizarrón
2. _____ el cuaderno   **b.** el carro
3. _____ la pizarra   **c.** la libreta, el bloc
4. _____ el libro de texto   **d.** la calificación
5. _____ el coche   **e.** no privado
6. _____ público   **f.** el libro escolar
7. _____ la asignatura   **g.** aproximadamente
8. _____ a eso de   **h.** el curso

F **La escuela y los cursos.** Tell whether each statement is true or false.

1. _____ Un curso aburrido es también interesante.
2. _____ Es fácil sacar notas buenas o altas en un curso muy difícil.
3. _____ En una escuela elemental o primaria, el maestro o la maestra enseña muchos cursos.
4. _____ En una escuela secundaria o superior, el profesor enseña uno o dos cursos.
5. _____ El alumno que estudia mucho es el alumno que saca notas malas o bajas.
6. _____ El alumno toma apuntes en una pizarra.
7. _____ El alumno lleva los libros en una mochila.
8. _____ El profesor toma un examen.
9. _____ El alumno de biología usa un microscopio en el laboratorio.

ESTRUCTURA

El presente de los verbos en –ar
Formas singulares

A **Preguntas personales.** Give your own answers.

1. ¿Qué lengua hablas en la clase de español?

_____

2. ¿Qué lengua hablas en casa?

_____

3. ¿A qué hora llegas a la escuela?

_____

4. ¿Cómo llegas a la escuela?

_____

5. ¿Cuántos cursos tomas en un semestre?

_____

6. ¿Qué notas sacas?

_____

7. ¿Estudias mucho?

_____

8. ¿Miras la pizarra?

_____

B **El profesor y yo.** Complete each sentence with the appropriate word(s).

1. El profesor _____ y yo _____ apuntes en el cuaderno.
2. Yo _____ la lección y el profesor _____ o presenta la lección.
3. Yo no _____ uniforme a la escuela y el profesor no _____ uniforme.
4. Yo _____ los libros escolares en una mochila.
5. Yo _____ a la escuela a las ocho pero el profesor _____ a eso de las siete y media.

C **Una carta.** Write a letter to a new pen pal in a Spanish-speaking country. In the first paragraph, tell: *quién eres, de dónde eres, de qué nacionalidad eres, cómo eres, dónde eres alumno.* In the second paragraph, tell: *en qué escuela estudias, a qué hora llegas, cómo llegas, quién es el / la profesor(a) de español, cómo es el / la profesor(a), cómo es la clase de español.*

Tú y usted

D **Profesor(a).** Make up five questions you want to ask a teacher.

1. _____

2. _____

3. _____

4. _____

5. _____

E   **Amigo(a).** Make up five questions you want to ask a friend.

1. _____

2. _____

3. _____

4. _____

5. _____

F   **¿Eres tú…? ¿Es Ud.…?** Ask questions of the people in the pictures using the cues.

1. señor López/enseñar (el) español

    _____

2. Elena/estudiar mucho

    _____

3. Tomás/tomar apuntes

    _____

4. doña Lucía/hablar alemán

    _____

Nombre _____ Fecha _____

UN POCO MÁS

A **Las notas.** Look at Elena's report card. Based on her report card, give the following information.

EXPLICACIÓN DE SIGLAS

INSTITUTO NACIONAL DE BACHILLERATO
"SANTA TERESA DE JESÚS"
Fomento, núm 9 • MADRID • 13

C: Conocimientos.

SB	Sobresaliente
NT	Notable
B	Bien
SF	Suficiente
IS	Insuficiente
MD	Muy deficiente

BOLETÍN DE NOTAS

DE LA ALUMNA

Elena Ruíz de las Rivas
Lope de Vega, 90
68-0976
_____

Ac: Actitud.

A	Muy buena
B	Buena
C	Normal
D	Pasiva
E	Negativa

Curso C. O. U.
Grupo **1**

CURSO ACADÉMICO
__94__ 19 __95__

Escobar de Cruz

DE VISITAS DE PADRES
Horas:

ALUMNA Elena Ruíz de las Rivas   Número **26** Curso C. O. U.

SESIONES DE EVALUACIÓN

MATERIAS	1" C	1" Ac	1" AG	2" C	2" Ac	2" AG
Seminario de Lengua Española	NT	B	S	NT	B	S
Filosofía	SB	A	S	SB	A	S
Lengua Extranjera Inglés	B	B	S	SF	B	S
Literatura	B	C	RC	B	C	RC
H.• del Mundo Contemporáneo	NT	B	S	NT	B	S
Latín				B	A	S
Griego	SF	C	RC	SF	B	RC
H.• del Arte	B	B	S			
Matemáticas	NT	A	S	SB	A	S
Física	B	C	S	NT	B	S
Química	SF	D	RA	IS	D	RR
Biología						
Geología						
Dibujo Técnico						

1. en qué escuela estudia _____

2. qué cursos toma _____

   _____

3. qué nota saca en español _____

4. qué nota saca en matemáticas _____

B **Actitud.** Look at Elena's report card again. Write the terms used to describe a student's attitude.

1. _____   4. _____

2. _____   5. _____

3. _____

C **Conocimiento.** Look at the report card again. Write the terms used to describe a student's achievement.

1. _____   4. _____

2. _____   5. _____

3. _____   6. _____

D **El Almanaque del Mundo.** The World Almanac gives a lot of interesting details. Read what it has to say about education in several Spanish-speaking countries.

México La educación primaria (ciclo de seis años) es gratuita y obligatoria en el país. La preparatoria dura tres años igual que la secundaria, que no es obligatoria.

Colombia La educación primaria es gratuita y obligatoria entre los seis y los doce años. La educación secundaria tiene una duración de seis años y otorga los grados de bachiller clásico, pedagógico o educación vocacional.

Argentina La enseñanza es gratuita desde el nivel preescolar hasta el universitario, y obligatoria desde seis a catorce años de edad. La enseñanza secundaria tiene una duración entre cuatro y seis años y es requisito indispensable para cursar estudios superiores.

Puerto Rico La educación es obligatoria entre los seis y los dieciséis años. La primaria consta de seis grados; la secundaria está dividida en dos ciclos de tres años cada uno. Tanto la enseñanza preprimaria como la vocacional de nivel secundaria forman parte de la educación pública. Hay también numerosas escuelas privadas en el país.

España La educación primaria comienza a los seis años de edad y dura cinco años. La educación básica general es obligatoria y gratuita desde los seis años hasta los catorce y puede ser extendida hasta los dieciséis. La escuela secundaria comienza a los once años de edad y dura siete años y tiene dos ciclos. El primero es la continuación de la educación básica.

E **La educación.** Tell whether each statement is true or false.

1. _____ La educación primaria en México es de seis años.
2. _____ La educación secundaria es obligatoria en México.
3. _____ La educación primaria es obligatoria en Colombia.
4. _____ La educación secundaria en Colombia es de seis años y no es obligatoria.
5. _____ La educación en la Argentina es gratuita.
6. _____ La educación universitaria es también gratuita en la Argentina.
7. _____ La educación primaria consta de ocho años en Puerto Rico.
8. _____ La educación no es gratuita en España.

F **Buscando informes.** Until what age is education required in each of the following countries?

1. _____ México
2. _____ Colombia
3. _____ Argentina
4. _____ Puerto Rico
5. _____ España

G **¿Dónde?** Write down the name of the country where each of the following is true.

1. _____ La enseñanza preprimaria forma parte de la educación pública.
2. _____ La escuela secundaria tiene dos ciclos.
3. _____ La educación secundaria otorga el grado de bachiller.
4. _____ La preparatoria no es obligatoria.
5. _____ Hay muchas escuelas privadas.
6. _____ La enseñanza preescolar es gratuita.
7. _____ El ciclo primero es la continuación de la educación básica.
8. _____ La enseñanza secundaria es indispensable para cursar estudios superiores.

MI AUTOBIOGRAFÍA

Continue with your autobiography. Write about your life as a student. Write about your life as a student. Tell some things you do in school each day. When do you arrive to school? How do you get there? Do you wear a uniform?

Mi autobiografía

PASATIEMPOS
DESPUÉS DE LAS CLASES

VOCABULARIO

Palabras 1

A ¿Qué es? Write the name of each item.

1. _____   2. _____   3. _____

4. _____   5. _____   6. _____

B **Después de las clases.** Complete each sentence with the appropriate word(s).

1. Después de las clases, los amigos _____ a casa a pie.
2. Los amigos _____ discos y _____ la televisión.
3. Los amigos _____ una merienda en la cocina.
4. Los amigos _____ por teléfono.
5. Carlos y María _____ en una tienda de discos después de las clases.

Palabras 2

C **Una fiesta.** Write a sentence about each of the following people according to the illustration.

1. Elena _____

2. Emilio _____

3. Nando y Marisa _____

D **¿Divertido o serio?** Tell whether each of the following activities is *divertido* or *serio.*

1. _____ escuchar discos
2. _____ bailar
3. _____ estudiar
4. _____ tomar un examen
5. _____ dar una fiesta
6. _____ tocar el piano
7. _____ trabajar
8. _____ mirar la televisión
9. _____ cantar en el coro
10. _____ tocar en la orquesta

E **Expresiones.** Match the verb in the left column with an appropriate word or expression in the right column.

1. dar _____   cintas
2. invitar _____   el tango argentino
3. cantar _____   el piano
4. bailar _____   a los amigos
5. tocar _____   una canción popular
6. tomar _____   una fiesta
7. escuchar _____   un refresco

F **Actividades divertidas.** Write sentences using each expression in Exercise E.

1. _____
2. _____
3. _____
4. _____
5. _____
6. _____
7. _____

ESTRUCTURA

El presente de los verbos en –ar
Formas plurales

A **En la fiesta.** Rewrite the sentences changing *El muchacho* to *Los muchachos*. Make all other necessary changes.

1. El muchacho canta.

   _____

2. El muchacho toca la guitarra.

   _____

3. El muchacho habla.

   _____

4. El muchacho toma un refresco.

   _____

5. El muchacho escucha cintas.

   _____

B **En la escuela.** Complete the following mini-conversations.

1. —¿Cuántos cursos tomas?

   —¿Yo? Yo _____ cinco.

   —¿Sí? Nosotros también _____ cinco cursos.

2. —¿A qué hora llegas a la escuela?

   —¿Yo? Yo _____ a la escuela a las ocho menos cinco.

   —¿Sí? Nosotros también _____ a las ocho menos cinco.

3. —¿Qué nota sacas en español?

   —¿Yo? Yo _____ _____ en español.

   —¿Sí? Nosotros también _____ _____ en español.

4. —¿Trabajas mucho en la escuela?

   —Sí. Yo _____ mucho.

   —Nosotros también _____ mucho.

   Pero los amigos no _____ mucho.

C **¿Y Uds.?** Complete each sentence with the correct form of the indicated verb.

1. (estudiar)

   Nosotros _____ español.

   ¿Qué lengua extranjera _____ Uds.?

2. (trabajar)

   Nosotros _____ en una tienda.

   ¿Dónde _____ Uds.?

3. (hablar)

   Nosotros _____ inglés en casa.

   ¿Qué lengua _____ Uds. en casa?

4. (tocar)

   Nosotros _____ el piano.

   ¿Qué instrumento musical _____ Uds.?

D **Carolina la curiosa.** Complete the following conversation about yourself and a friend using the correct form of the indicated verbs.

CAROLINA: ¿A qué hora _____ tú y Roberto a casa después de las clases?
            1
(llegar)

TÚ: Pues, nosotros _____ a casa a las tres y media. (llegar)
                    2

CAROLINA: ¿_____ Uds. una merienda? (tomar)
            3

TÚ: Sí, _____ una merienda. (tomar)
        4

CAROLINA: ¿Quién _____ la merienda? (preparar)
                  5

TÚ: A veces yo _____ la merienda y a veces Roberto
                6

_____ la merienda. (preparar, preparar)
        7

CAROLINA: ¿_____ Uds. discos? (escuchar)
            8

TÚ: No. Nosotros _____ casetes o cintas. Yo
                 9

_____ jazz y Roberto _____
        10   11

rock. (escuchar, escuchar, escuchar)

CAROLINA: Yo no _____ discos. Yo _____ la
                12   13

televisión. (escuchar, mirar)

E **Actividades diarias.** Form sentences according to the model.

Yo / mirar
Yo miro la televisión en la sala con un amigo.

1. Juan / preparar

_____

2. Nosotros / trabajar

_____

3. Carlos y Felipe / escuchar

_____

4. Bárbara / hablar

_____

5. Tú / estudiar

_____

6. Nosotros / tocar

_____

7. Uds. / trabajar

_____

El presente de los verbos ir, dar y estar

F **La clase de español.** Complete each sentence with the correct form of the indicated verb.

1. Yo _____ a la clase de español a las diez de la mañana. (ir)
2. Yo _____ en la clase de español hasta las once menos cuarto. (estar)
3. Yo _____ las gracias a la profesora de español. Ella es muy simpática. (dar)
4. Yo _____ a casa a eso de las tres. (ir)
5. Yo _____ en casa con mis amigos después de las clases. (estar)

G **¿Qué profesor?** Complete each sentence with the correct form of the indicated verb.

1. El profesor de biología _____ muchos exámenes. (dar)

2. El profesor de inglés y el profesor de historia no _____ muchos exámenes. (dar)

3. Desde las tres hasta las cuatro el profesor de biología siempre _____ en el laboratorio. (estar)

4. Él _____ al laboratorio para preparar las lecciones. (ir)

5. A veces yo _____ al laboratorio. (ir)

6. Cuando yo _____ en el laboratorio, trabajo con un microscopio. (estar)

H **¿Y Uds.?** Complete each mini-conversation with the correct form of the indicated verb.

1. (dar)

—¿Tú _____ una fiesta?

—¿Quién? ¿Yo? No, yo no _____ una fiesta. ¿De qué fiesta hablas?

2. (ir)

—¿Tú _____ a la fiesta de Marta?

—Sí, _____. ¿Tú _____ también?

—¡Claro! Yo _____ con Sandra.

—¿Cómo _____ Uds.?

—Nosotros _____ en carro.

3. (estar)

—Roberto, ¿cómo _____?

— _____ bien.

—¿Tú _____ bien? ¿Seguro?

—Pues, así, así.

—Hombre, ¿_____ enfermo?

—No, no. No _____ enfermo. Pero _____ nervioso.

—¿Por qué?

—Porque mañana es el examen final de español.

I **Alfredo y Teresa.** Write sentences about Alfredo and Teresa according to the illustrations. Use *ir, dar,* or *estar* in your sentences.

1. _____

    _____

2. _____

    _____

3. _____

    _____

Las contracciones al y del

J **Después de las clases.** Complete with *a* or *de* and the correct definite article, if necessary.

Roberto es _____ Estados Unidos. ¿De qué estado es? Él es
                                    1

_____ estado de Nueva York. Después _____ clases,
         2   3

Roberto no va _____ casa. Y él no va _____ café. Él va
                       4   5

_____ tienda donde trabaja a tiempo parcial. En la tienda él escucha
         6

_____ clientes.
         7

K **En el laboratorio.** Complete with *a* or *de* and the correct definite article, if necessary.

1. El amigo _____ muchacha cubana va _____ laboratorio.

2. La amiga _____ muchacho ecuatoriano no va _____
   laboratorio. Ella va _____ clase de historia.

3. En el laboratorio los alumnos miran _____ profesor.

UN POCO MÁS

A **Una invitación.** Read the following invitation.

> *José M.ª Carrascal Gómez*
> *M.ª Luisa Gil Juárez*
>
> *Tienen el gusto de invitarles a una fiesta*
> *en honor de su hija*
> *Mónica*
> *en la ocasión de su quinceañera*
> *que se celebrará el día siete de agosto,*
> *a las diecinueve horas.*
>
> *Cena en casa*
> *Miguel Ángel, 14-1º*
> *Madrid*

B **Una fiesta.** In a word or two, give the following information according to the invitation.

1. Who is the guest of honor?

_____

2. What is the occasion for the party?

_____

3. Who is giving the party?

_____

4. When is the party?

_____

5. Where is the party?

_____

6. Will there be food served at the party?

_____

C **Un poco de geografía.** Read the following. Guess the meanings of any words you do not know.

> España es un país. Está en Europa. La capital de España es Madrid. España y Portugal forman una península—la península ibérica. Es una península porque hay agua a los tres lados—el mar Mediterráneo, el océano Atlántico y el mar Cantábrico. Al norte entre Francia y España están los Pirineos. Los Pirineos son montañas. Forman la frontera entre Francia y España.

D **España.** Tell whether each statement is true or false.

1. _____ España es una isla.
2. _____ España es un continente.
3. _____ España y Francia forman una península.
4. _____ Los Pirineos son montañas.
5. _____ Madrid es la capital de España.

E **Una pregunta.** Choose the word or expression that best completes each sentence.

1. España es _____.
   a. un continente
   b. un país
   c. una frontera

2. El Mediterráneo es _____.
   a. una montaña
   b. un océano
   c. un mar

3. España y Portugal forman _____.
   a. una península
   b. una frontera
   c. un mar

4. _____ está al norte de España.
   a. Portugal
   b. Italia
   c. Francia

5. Hay _____ entre Francia y España.
   a. montañas
   b. un mar
   c. un continente

MI AUTOBIOGRAFÍA

Continue with your autobiography. Tell some things you or you and your friends do after school. If you have a part-time job, be sure to write about it.

Mi autobiografía

SELF-TEST 1

A   Match the word in the left column with its opposite in the right column.

1. _____ alto   **a.** moreno
2. _____ aburrido   **b.** el alumno
3. _____ rubio   **c.** antipático
4. _____ grande   **d.** bajo
5. _____ el profesor   **e.** malo
6. _____ bueno   **f.** interesante
7. _____ a pie   **g.** pequeño
8. _____ simpático   **h.** en carro

B   Write the name of each item.

1. _____ 2. _____ 3. _____

 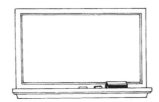 

4. _____ 5. _____ 6. _____

7. _____ 8. _____

C Match the verb in the left column with an appropriate expression in the right column.

1.	hablar _____	un(a) alumno(a) serio(a)
2.	escuchar _____	un examen
3.	ser _____	por teléfono
4.	dar _____	en autobús
5.	tomar _____	a las ocho
6.	trabajar _____	la lección
7.	ir _____	la televisión
8.	estudiar _____	discos
9.	llegar _____	una fiesta
10.	mirar _____	en una tienda
11.	tocar _____	el tango
12.	bailar _____	una merienda
13.	preparar _____	el piano

D Give your own answers.

1. ¿Quién eres?

_____

2. ¿De qué nacionalidad eres?

_____

3. ¿Qué lengua hablas?

_____

4. ¿Cuántos cursos tomas?

_____

5. ¿A qué hora llegas a la escuela?

_____

6. ¿A qué escuela vas?

_____

7. ¿Dónde estás ahora?

_____

E Complete each sentence with the correct form of the indicated verb(s).

1. Ellos _____ amigos. (ser)

2. Él y yo (nosotros) _____ alumnos en la misma escuela. (ser)

3. Nosotros _____ a la escuela en el bus escolar. (ir)

4. ¿A qué hora _____ tú a la escuela? (llegar)

5. ¿Cuántos cursos _____ tú? (tomar)

6. Yo _____ español. (estudiar)

7. La profesora de español _____ muy simpática. (ser)

8. Nosotros _____ en la clase de español ahora. (estar)

9. En la clase de español los alumnos _____, _____ y
    _____ apuntes. (escuchar, hablar, tomar)

10. Después de las clases yo _____ al centro comercial. (ir)

11. Adela y Tomás _____ muchas fiestas buenas. (dar)

F Form sentences using *ser.*

1. El muchacho / alto

    _____

2. Las muchachas / sincero

    _____

3. Los cursos / interesante

    _____

4. La profesora / amable

    _____

5. Las clases / grande

    _____

6. Los hermanos / popular

    _____

7. La lección / difícil

    _____

G Complete with *a* or *de* and the correct definite article, if necessary.

1. Llegamos _____ escuela a las ocho.
2. Y después _____ clases vamos _____ centro comercial.
3. Yo invito a Teresa _____ fiesta.
4. Hablamos _____ curso de biología.
5. Hablamos _____ profesores también.

H Choose the word or expression that best completes each sentence.

1. En Latinoamérica el colegio es _____.
   a. una escuela primaria
   b. una escuela secundaria
   c. una universidad
2. Puerto Rico es una parte de _____.
   a. España
   b. una isla
   c. los Estados Unidos
3. Puerto Rico es _____.
   a. una isla
   b. una península
   c. un mar
4. _____ es la capital del Ecuador.
   a. San Juan
   b. Bogotá
   c. Quito
5. Muchos jóvenes trabajan a tiempo parcial en _____.
   a. los Estados Unidos
   b. España
   c. Latinoamérica
6. Hay muchas _____ en un centro comercial.
   a. casas
   b. tiendas
   c. escuelas

Answers appear on pages 177–178.

ACTIVIDADES DEL HOGAR

VOCABULARIO

Palabras 1

A **Un edificio.** Answer according to the illustration.

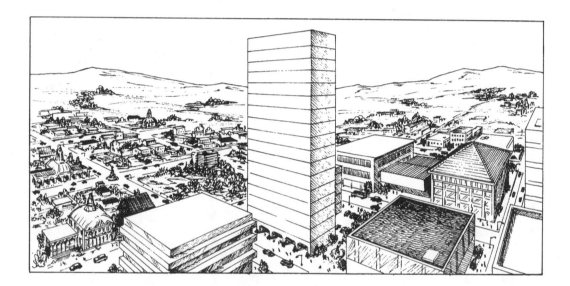

1. ¿Es grande o pequeño el edificio?

   _____

2. ¿Es un edificio alto o bajo?

   _____

3. ¿Está en una ciudad grande o en un pueblo pequeño el edificio?

   _____

4. ¿Está en el centro de la ciudad o en las afueras de la ciudad?

   _____

B **Lo contrario.** Match the word in the left column with its opposite in the right column.

1. _____ la planta baja   **a.** la ciudad
2. _____ las afueras   **b.** el apartamento
3. _____ el pueblo   **c.** el centro (de la ciudad)
4. _____ a la derecha   **d.** el piso superior
5. _____ la casa particular   **e.** a la izquierda
6. _____ alto   **f.** público
7. _____ grande   **g.** pequeño
8. _____ privado   **h.** bajo

C **Una ciudad grande.** Complete each sentence with the appropriate word(s).

1. Nueva York es una _____ grande.

2. En las _____ de la ciudad de Nueva York hay muchos suburbios.

3. En Nueva York hay muchos _____ muy altos. Son rascacielos.

4. En Nueva York hay muchos _____ pero no hay muchas casas
   _____.

5. Las personas que viven en los apartamentos de los pisos altos de los rascacielos no toman la
   escalera. _____ al apartamento en un _____.

6. Hay muchos _____ en los apartamentos. Son muy grandes.

7. La familia prepara la comida en la _____, come en el _____
   y mira la televisión en la _____.

D **¿Qué piso?** Express the information in the left column another way.

1. el piso número dos   el _____ piso
2. el piso número cuatro   el _____ piso
3. el piso número seis   el _____ piso
4. el piso número uno   el _____ piso
5. el piso número tres   el _____ piso
6. el piso número ocho   el _____ piso
7. el piso número siete   el _____ piso
8. el piso número nueve   el _____ piso
9. el piso número cinco   el _____ piso
10. el piso número diez   el _____ piso

Palabras 2

E ¿Qué es? Write the name of each item.

1. _____   2. _____   3. _____

4. _____   5. _____   6. _____

F **Expresiones.** Match the verb in the left column with one or more appropriate expressions in the right column.

1. leer _____   con bolígrafo
2. comer _____   las noticias
3. beber _____   el periódico
4. escribir _____   una carta
5. ver _____   una gaseosa

                                                                                  un sándwich

                                                                                  una emisión deportiva

                                                                                  un café

G **Lo contrario.** Match the word in the left column with its opposite in the right column.

1. _____ aprender   **a.** comprar
2. _____ escribir   **b.** bajar
3. _____ vender   **c.** leer
4. _____ comer   **d.** beber
5. _____ subir   **e.** enseñar

ESTRUCTURA

El presente de los verbos en –er *e* –ir

A **Expresiones.** Match the verb in the left column with an appropriate expression in the right column.

1. comer _____   el periódico
2. beber _____   por la escalera
3. vender _____   un sándwich
4. leer _____   en una casa privada
5. vivir _____   una gaseosa
6. subir _____   una carta
7. escribir _____   discos en una tienda

B **Paco.** Write sentences about Paco, telling what he does. Use each expression in Exercise A.

1. _____
2. _____
3. _____
4. _____
5. _____
6. _____
7. _____

C **Las dos hermanas.** Rewrite the sentences in Exercise B, changing *Paco* to *Las dos hermanas*.

1. _____
2. _____
3. _____
4. _____
5. _____
6. _____
7. _____

D **Preguntas personales.** Give your own answers.

1. ¿Dónde vives?

    _____

2. ¿Viven Uds. en una casa privada o en un apartamento?

    _____

3. ¿Comes con la familia?

    _____

4. ¿Comen Uds. en la cocina o en el comedor?

    _____

5. ¿Lees el periódico?

    _____

6. ¿Qué periódico leen Uds.?

    _____

7. ¿Ves la televisión?

    _____

8. ¿Qué emisiones ven Uds.?

    _____

E **En casa.** Rewrite the following story, changing *yo* to *nosotros*.

Yo vivo en el campo. Vivo en una casa particular. Como en la cocina.
Después de la comida, leo el periódico en la sala o veo la televisión.
A veces escribo una carta a un amigo.

_____

_____

_____

_____

_____

F **En la escuela.** Complete each mini-conversation with the correct form of the indicated verb.

1. (comprender)

   —Oye, Sandra, ¿_____ tú la lección?

   —Sí, _____ la lección.

2. (aprender)

   Sandra, ¿_____ mucho en la escuela?

   —Sí, sí. _____ mucho.

3. (recibir)

   —Sandra, ¿_____ (tú) notas muy altas?

   —Pues, a veces _____ notas altas pero no siempre.

4. (escribir)

   —Sandra y Tomás, ¿_____ Uds. muchas composiciones
   para la clase de inglés?

   —Sí, _____ muchas.

5. (comprender)

   —Sandra y Tomás, ¿_____ Uds. las instrucciones en el
   laboratorio de física?

   —Sí, _____ las instrucciones.

G **La televisión.** Rewrite the sentences changing *mirar* to *ver*.

1. Yo miro la televisión.

   _____

2. A las seis de la tarde miramos las noticias.

   _____

3. ¿Miras muchas emisiones deportivas?

   _____

4. Ellas miran una telenovela.

   _____

5. Ella mira un documental sobre el conflicto en el Perú.

   _____

Sustantivos en –dad, –tad, –ión

H **Otra palabra.** Write a noun related to each of the following adjectives.

1. responsable _____

2. popular _____

3. oportuno _____

4. capaz _____

La expresión impersonal hay

I **¿Qué hay?** Write five sentences about the illustration. Use *hay*.

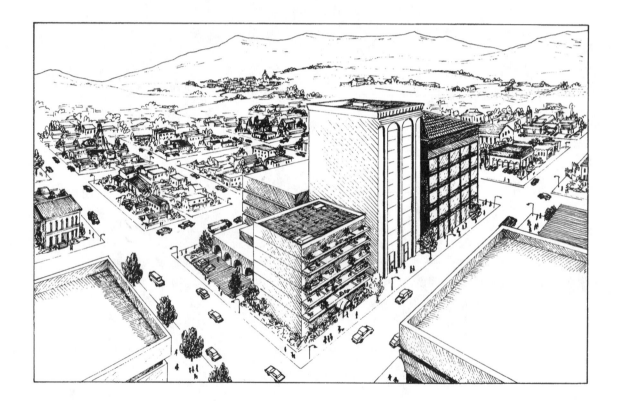

1. _____

2. _____

3. _____

4. _____

5. _____

UN POCO MÁS

A **Un anuncio.** Read the following real estate ad that appeared recently in the Bolivian newspaper *El Diario.*

B **Para vender.** Answer the following questions with a word or phrase according to the ad.

1. ¿Qué venden?

   _____

2. ¿Cuántos pisos hay?

   _____

3. ¿Cuántos cuartos de dormir hay?

   _____

4. ¿Cuál es el precio?

   _____

> Vendo **CASA**
> llena de sol, hermosa vista,
> todas las dependencias
> - 2 plantas
> - garaje para varios carros
> - 3 dormitorios
> - terreno plano de 412 metros
>
> ## $US 67.000
>
> *Alberto Ostria No. 1277 (Cristo Rey)*

C **Otra palabra.** What word does the ad use for each of the following?

1. pisos _____
2. coches _____
3. cuartos de dormir _____
4. bonita, preciosa _____

D **Adivinen.** Figure it out or guess according to the ad.

1. How does the ad describe the garage?

   _____

2. What are the dimensions of the property?

   _____

3. What does the word *plano* probably mean?

   _____

4. The dictionary definition of *dependencia* is: *Cada habitación o espacio dedicado a los servicios de una casa.* What does *dependencia* probably mean?

   _____

E **Lima, la capital del Perú.** Read the following about Lima. Guess the meanings of any unfamiliar words.

Lima es una ciudad grande de la América Latina. Es la capital del Perú. En el centro de la ciudad de Lima hay muchas plazas bonitas con edificios antiguos de estilo colonial. Los edificios antiguos no son muy altos. En las calles del centro de la capital, el Jirón de la Unión, por ejemplo, hay muchos ambulantes. Los ambulantes venden todo tipo de mercancías.

En las afueras de Lima, cerca de la costa del Pacífico, hay suburbios bonitos y elegantes como Miraflores y San Isidro. En las calles y avenidas bordadas de palmas hay mansiones lujosas y edificios altos con modernos departamentos (apartamentos) elegantes. El autor contemporáneo peruano, Vargas Llosa, describe la vida de Lima y de sus suburbios en sus novelas de fama mundial.

F **Estudio de palabras.** Match the word in the left column with a definition or equivalent in the right column.

1. _____ antiguo   **a.** elegante
2. _____ ambulante   **b.** objetos para vender
3. _____ mercancías   **c.** de hoy, no del pasado
4. _____ una mansión   **d.** dar una descripción
5. _____ lujoso   **e.** del pasado, viejo
6. _____ contemporáneo **f.** una casa grande y elegante
7. _____ describir   **g.** que anda o va a pie

G **Buscando informes.** In a word or two, give the following information according to the reading in Exercise E.

1. the name of an author _____

2. the names of two suburbs of Lima _____

3. the ocean near Lima _____

4. the name of a main street in Lima _____

H **Frases.** Write four original sentences about Lima.

1. _____

2. _____

3. _____

4. _____

I **En el periódico.** Read the following headlines to an article that appeared recently in *El Comercio,* a newspaper in Quito, Ecuador.

ASTROS Y SIGNOS

Todos los días en diarios y revistas aparece el horóscopo. Miles de jóvenes y adultos leen las "predicciones". ¿Por qué seduce tanto el horóscopo? Los jóvenes del Club de Periodismo consultan sobre este fascinante tema.

J **¿De qué se trata?** Tell what the headlines are about.

_____

_____

_____

_____

K **Estudio de palabras.** Match the word in the left column with a word or expression that means the same in the right column.

1. _____ el diario   **a.** atrae (atracción)

2. _____ los jóvenes   **b.** personas mayores de 21 años

3. _____ los adultos   **c.** el periódico

4. _____ seduce (seducción) **d.** muy interesante

5. _____ fascinante   **e.** muchachos y muchachas

MI AUTOBIOGRAFÍA

Continue with your autobiography. Write about where you live and describe your house or apartment. Be sure to give your address. Also, tell about some things you and your family do at home. When do you eat dinner? Who prepares dinner? What do you do after dinner? If you read the newspaper, tell which one you read. Do you watch television? Tell which programs you watch. Be sure to tell some things other members of your family do.

Mi autobiografía

CAPÍTULO 6

LA FAMILIA Y SU CASA

VOCABULARIO

Palabras 1

A **El árbol genealógico.** Write the relationship of each person to Adela.

B **Una familia.** Complete each sentence with the appropriate word(s).

1. Una familia grande tiene muchas _____ y una familia pequeña tiene

   pocas _____.

2. Una persona que tiene quince años es _____ y una persona que tiene

   noventa años es _____.

3. Un _____ o un gato es una mascota.

4. El _____ y el _____ son animales domésticos.

Palabras 2

C **¿Qué es?** Write the name of each item.

1. _____ 2. _____ 3. _____

4. _____ 5. _____ 6. _____

7. _____ 8. _____

D **¿Qué es?** Complete each sentence with the appropriate word(s).

1. Un sedán es un tipo de _____.

2. Un ciclomotor es un tipo de _____ con motor.

3. Hay árboles, plantas y flores en un _____ o en un _____.

4. La palma es un tipo de _____.

5. El _____ de una casa es para el coche.

E **El cumpleaños.** Complete with appropriate words.

Hoy es el _____ de Diana. Ella _____ catorce años. Sus
          1   2

padres dan una _____ en su honor para celebrar su _____.
                    3   4

Los padres _____ a los amigos y a los parientes de Diana a la fiesta. Diana
                    5

recibe muchos _____.
                    6

F **La fiesta.** Write a list of activities that take place at a party.

_____

_____

_____

_____

_____

_____

_____

_____

_____

_____

_____

ESTRUCTURA

El presente del verbo tener

A **Preguntas personales.** Give your own answers.

1. ¿Cuántos hermanos tienes?

_____

2. ¿Tienes tíos?

_____

3. ¿Tienes primos también? Si tienes primos, ¿cuántos tienes?

_____

4. ¿Tienes abuelos?

_____

5. ¿Cuántos años tienes?

_____

6. ¿Tienes una mascota?

_____

7. Si tienes una mascota, ¿qué tienes?

_____

B **La edad.** Give the age of each member of your immediate family.

_____

_____

_____

_____

_____

_____

_____

C **¿Qué tiene?** Tell what each person has. Form sentences using *tener.*

1. Ella / perro

   _____

2. Ellos / coche grande

   _____

3. Yo / bicicleta

   _____

4. Nosotros / casa privada

   _____

5. Uds. / apartamento elegante

   _____

6. Tú / ciclomotor

   _____

Tener que + *el infinitivo*

D **Es necesario.** Answer using *tener que.*

1. ¿Qué tienes que hacer en la clase de inglés?

   _____

2. ¿Qué tienen Uds. que hacer en la clase de español?

   _____

3. ¿A qué hora tienen que llegar a la escuela los alumnos?

   _____

4. ¿Qué tiene que preparar un miembro de la familia en la cocina?

   _____

5. ¿Qué tienes que comprar para el cumpleaños de un(a) pariente?

   _____

Ir a + *el infinitivo*

E **Mañana.** Tell what each person is going to do tomorrow. Use *ir a.*

1. Yo doy una fiesta en honor de Adela.

_____

2. Paco cumple quince años.

_____

3. Tú escribes una composición para la clase de español.

_____

4. Los padres invitan a los abuelos a comer.

_____

5. Nosotros compramos un regalo para la abuela.

_____

Los adjetivos posesivos

F **Preguntas personales.** Give your own answers.

1. ¿Dónde viven tus abuelos?

_____

2. ¿Cuántos hijos tiene tu abuela materna?

_____

3. ¿Dónde trabaja tu madre o tu padre?

_____

4. ¿Tienes hermanos? ¿A qué escuela van tus hermanos? Si no tienes hermanos, ¿a qué escuela van tus amigos?

_____

G **Tareas.** Tell what each person has to do for his or her class. Use *mi*, *tu*, or *su*.

1. Carlos tiene que preparar un informe para _____ clase de inglés.

2. Yo tengo que escribir una composición para _____ clase de inglés.

3. Juan y Lupe tienen que preparar una conversación para _____ clase de español.

4. Tú tienes que resolver cuatro problemas para _____ clase de álgebra.

5. Elena tiene que escribir a _____ tía.

H **Los primos.** Tell about your cousins.

1. _____ primos viven en _____.

2. _____ casa está en la calle _____.

3. Su madre es _____ tía Dolores.

4. _____ tía Dolores, _____ madre, tiene una tienda.

5. En _____ tienda ella vende discos y videos.

I **Nuestra familia.** Rewrite the sentences changing *mi(s)* or *tu(s)* to *nuestro(s)* or *su(s)*.

1. ¿Cuántas personas hay en tu familia?

   _____

2. En mi familia hay cinco personas. Somos cinco.

   _____

3. ¿Viven tus abuelos en Madrid?

   _____

4. No, mis abuelos viven en México.

   _____

5. ¿Visitan mucho tus abuelos?

   _____

UN POCO MÁS

A **Un matrimonio.** Read the following wedding announcement that appeared in the newspaper *El Mercurio* in Santiago de Chile.

Matrimonio
González Parra-Diez del Corral Pérez-Soba

Hoy, a las 13 horas, en el monasterio de Armentetra (Pontevedra, España), se efectuará el matrimonio de Pilar Diez del Corral Pérez-Soba con Gastón González Parra. Serán padrinos de la novia don Jesús Diez del Corral Rivas y señora Pilar Pérez-Soba Baro, y del novio, don Gastón González Palacios y señora Carmen Parra Rodríguez.

B **Información.** In a word or two, answer the questions according to the wedding announcement.

1. ¿A qué hora es la ceremonia?

_____

2. ¿En qué país es la ceremonia?

_____

3. ¿Qué es "Armentetra"?

_____

C **Adivinen.** Figure it out or guess.

1. Who is the bride?

_____

2. Who is the groom?

_____

3. Who is probably the groom's mother?

_____

4. Who is probably the bride's father?

_____

D **Felicidades.** Look at the card and read it.

MUCHAS
FELICIDADES
*En Tus
Quince Años*

Ya cumples quince años
Un cumpleaños especial,
Para una señorita,
Es una ocasión sentimental.

Siempre tendrás memorias
De amigas muy sinceras,
De regalos y de fiestas,
De tus quince primaveras.

Y después tú vas a pensar
En este año particular
Y sé que vas a recordar el día
Con lágrimas de alegría.

E **¿Qué dice?** In a word or two, answer the questions according to the card.

1. ¿Para qué es la tarjeta?

    _____

2. ¿Cuántos años cumple la muchacha?

    _____

3. ¿Cómo es la ocasión?

    _____

4. ¿De qué va a tener memorias la muchacha?

    _____

Nombre _____ Fecha _____

F **Para vender.** Read the following advertisement that appeared in a Spanish newspaper.

G **El anuncio.** Choose the word or expression that best completes each statement according to the advertisement.

1. Los apartamentos están en _____.
   a. Chile
   b. España
   c. Puerto Rico

2. Los apartamentos más grandes tienen _____ dormitorios.
   a. tres
   b. cinco
   c. diez

3. Los apartamentos están cerca de _____.
   a. un hotel
   b. un teléfono
   c. un mar

4. Los apartamentos están a diez kilómetros de la ciudad de _____.
   a. Alicante
   b. Mediterráneo
   c. Madrid

H **Las abreviaturas.** The following abbreviations are used in the advertisement you read. Try to find the abbreviation for each word.

1. kilómetro _____
2. pesetas _____
3. calle _____
4. tercero _____
5. avenida _____

MI AUTOBIOGRAFÍA

Write as much as you can about your family and your house. If you have a pet, be sure to mention him or her. Give the names and ages of each member of your family and describe each of them. Also tell where each person lives. Then write about where you live and describe your house or apartment. Be sure to include your address.

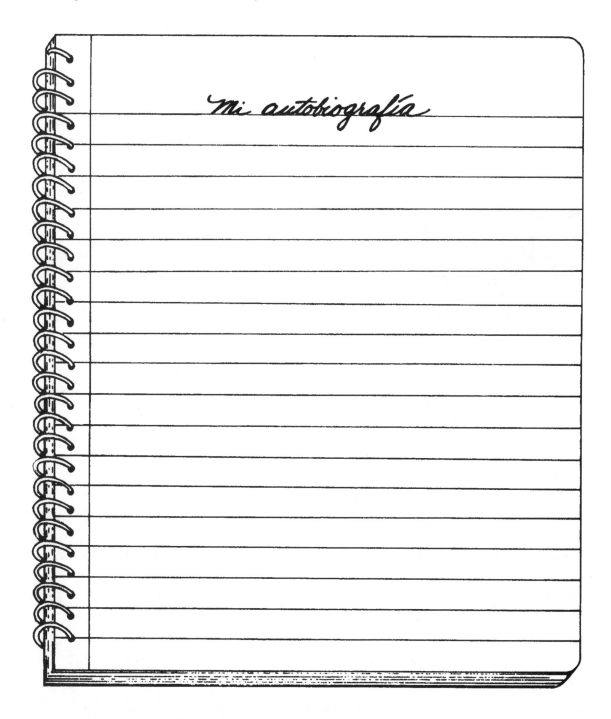

mi autobiografía

CAPÍTULO 7

LOS DEPORTES DE EQUIPO

VOCABULARIO

Palabras 1

A **¿Qué es?** Write the name of each item.

1. _____   2. _____   3. _____

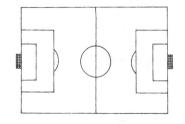

4. _____   5. _____

B **Un juego de fútbol.** Complete each sentence with the appropriate word(s).

1. El jugador _____ el balón con el pie.

2. El _____ guarda la portería.

3. El portero trata de parar o _____ el balón.

4. Si el balón entra en la portería, el otro jugador _____ un gol y su equipo

   marca un _____.

5. El tanto queda _____ cuando los dos equipos tienen el mismo tanto.

6. En un partido de fútbol hay dos _____.

C **Diccionario.** Write the word being defined.

1. el que juega _____
2. el que guarda la portería _____
3. una estación del año _____
4. el conjunto de jugadores _____
5. salir victorioso _____
6. no dejar (permitir) entrar _____
7. lo contrario de *ganar* _____
8. meter el balón en la portería _____

Palabras 2

D **Los deportes.** Write the names of four sports.

1. _____
2. _____
3. _____
4. _____

E **El baloncesto.** Write five words associated with basketball.

1. _____
2. _____
3. _____
4. _____
5. _____

F **El béisbol.** Write five words associated with baseball.

1. _____
2. _____
3. _____
4. _____
5. _____

G **El partido de béisbol.** Write as much as you can about the illustration.

_____

_____

_____

_____

_____

_____

_____

_____

_____

_____

_____

ESTRUCTURA

El presente de los verbos con el cambio e > ie

A **¿Jugar qué?** Rewrite the following sentences in the singular.

1. Queremos jugar (al) vólibol.

   _____

2. Preferimos jugar en el parque.

   _____

3. Empezamos a jugar a las dos y media.

   _____

4. Mis hermanos quieren jugar al fútbol.

   _____

5. Ellos prefieren jugar en el campo de la escuela.

   _____

6. Empiezan a jugar al mediodía.

   _____

B **Al café.** Rewrite the following sentences in the plural *(nosotros)*.

1. Quiero comer.

   _____

2. Prefiero ir al café Gijón.

   _____

3. Quiero un sándwich (un bocadillo).

   _____

4. Empiezo a comer.

   _____

5. No quiero postre.

   _____

C **El partido de hoy.** Complete each sentence with the correct form of the indicated verb.

1. Hoy nosotros _____ a jugar a las dos. (empezar)

2. Nosotros _____ ganar. No _____ perder. (querer, querer)

3. Si nosotros _____ el juego de hoy, _____ todo. (perder, perder)

D **El partido de hoy.** Rewrite each sentence in Exercise C, changing *nosotros* to *yo*.

1. _____

2. _____

3. _____

El presente de los verbos con el cambio o > ue

E **Cosas personales.** Complete each sentence with the correct form of the indicated verb.

1. Yo _____ ocho horas cada noche. (dormir)

2. Yo _____ llegar a la escuela a las ocho menos cuarto. (poder)

3. Yo _____ tomar el autobús a la escuela. (poder)

4. Yo _____ al fútbol después de las clases. (jugar)

5. Yo _____ con el equipo de la escuela. (jugar)

6. Yo _____ a casa a las cinco y media o a las seis. (volver)

7. Yo _____ muy bien después de jugar mucho. (dormir)

F **El plural.** Rewrite the sentences in Exercise E in the plural *(nosotros)*.

1. _____

2. _____

3. _____

4. _____

5. _____

6. _____

7. _____

G **Las mismas opiniones.** Complete each sentence with the correct forms of the indicated verb.

1. Yo _____ comer y Tomás _____ comer. Nosotros también _____ comer en el mismo restaurante. (querer)

2. Él _____ estudiar ciencias y su amigo _____ estudiar ciencias. Ellos _____ ir a la misma universidad. (querer)

3. Tú _____ jugar y yo _____ jugar. Nosotros _____ jugar con el mismo equipo. (poder)

4. Uds. _____ y nosotros _____, pero nosotros no _____ en el mismo dormitorio. (dormir)

Los adjetivos de nacionalidad

H **Nacionalidades.** Answer the following questions according to the model.

¿Es él de Puerto Rico?
Sí, es puertorriqueño.

1. ¿Es él de México? _____

2. ¿Es ella de Cuba? _____

3. ¿Son ellos de Panamá? _____

4. ¿Son ellos de Colombia? _____

5. ¿Es él de Alemania? _____

6. ¿Es su amigo de Inglaterra? _____

7. ¿Es ella de España? _____

8. ¿Es su amiga de Francia? _____

9. ¿Son ellos de Portugal? _____

10. ¿Son ellas del Japón? _____

11. ¿Es ella del Canadá? _____

12. ¿Son ellas de Nicaragua? _____

13. ¿Es ella de Chile? _____

14. ¿Es él de Irlanda? _____

UN POCO MÁS

A **Un partido.** Look at the admission ticket to a *Copa Libertadores* game.

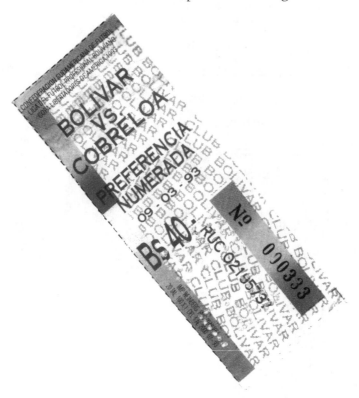

B **¿Sí o no?** Indicate whether each statement is true or false according to the ticket in Exercise A. If it is false, correct it.

1. El boleto es para un partido de tenis.

   _____

2. Cobreloa es un equipo de fútbol.

   _____

3. Cobreloa juega contra Libertadores.

   _____

4. Es un boleto para la Copa Mundial.

   _____

Nombre _____ Fecha _____

C **Las noticias deportivas.** Read the following article about the game in Exercise A, which appeared in *El Diario* of La Paz.

EN 30 MINUTOS SE DEFINIO EL PARTIDO

Con goles convertidos por Etcheverry, Borja y Baldivieso en el transcurso de 30 minutos del segundo período, el plantel de Bolívar se impuso a Cobreloa de Chile por 3 a 0, en partido válido para la Copa Libertadores de América, anoche en el estadio Olímpico de Miraflores ante más de 36.000 espectadores.

D **Información.** In a word or two, answer the questions according to the newspaper article.

1. What is the article about?

   _____

2. Who scored goals?

   _____

3. When did all the scoring take place?

   _____

4. What was the final score?

   _____

5. When was the game?

   _____

E **Buscando informes.** Find the following information in the newspaper article in Exercise C.

1. el nombre del estadio _____

2. el país que Cobreloa representa _____

3. el número de espectadores _____

MI AUTOBIOGRAFÍA

Write as much as you can about the sports teams at your school. Do you participate in any team sports? Tell which ones. Do you prefer to participate or to be a spectator? If you are not fond of sports, write about some of your other activities.

Mi autobiografía

UN VIAJE EN AVIÓN

VOCABULARIO

Palabras 1

A **Una tarjeta de embarque.** Give the following information according to the boarding pass.

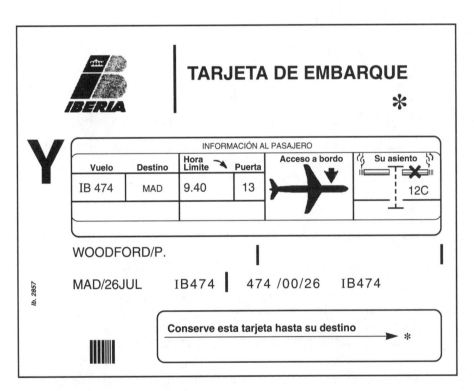

1. el nombre del pasajero _____

2. el nombre de la línea aérea _____

3. la hora de salida _____

4. la fecha del vuelo _____

5. el número del vuelo _____

6. el número de la puerta de salida _____

7. el número del asiento _____

8. el destino del vuelo _____

B **En el aeropuerto.** Tell whether each statement is true or false.

1. _____ Cuando el pasajero llega al aeropuerto, tiene que facturar las maletas grandes.
2. _____ Es imposible abordar el avión con el equipaje de mano.
3. _____ Cuando el pasajero factura su equipaje, el agente pone un talón en cada maleta para identificar el destino.
4. _____ Cuando uno hace un viaje internacional, es decir un viaje a un país extranjero, es necesario llevar (tener) pasaporte.
5. _____ Antes de abordar el avión, los pasajeros tienen que pasar por el control de seguridad donde inspeccionan al pasajero y su equipaje de mano. Verifican si el pasajero lleva un arma de fuego—como una pistola, por ejemplo.

C **Un viaje en avión.** Complete each sentence with the appropriate word(s).

1. Ella _____ un viaje en avión.
2. Ella _____ de casa en taxi para ir al aeropuerto.
3. Ella _____ sus maletas en la maletera del taxi.
4. Cuando llega al aeropuerto, ella _____ sus maletas en la báscula.
5. Ella _____ su equipaje. El agente _____ un talón en cada maleta.
6. Su avión _____ de la puerta de salida número siete.

D **La pantalla de salidas.** Choose the word or expression that best completes each sentence.

VUELO	SALIDA	ABORDAR	PUERTA	DESTINO
UA 105	7:05	6:30	5	BUENOS AIRES
AA 731	7:30	7:00	12	LIMA
AV 701	8:15	7:45	2	BOGOTÁ

1. El vuelo 105 de la United sale a las _____.
   a. siete y cinco
   b. seis y media
   c. cinco

2. El vuelo que sale a las ocho y cuarto va a _____.
   a. Lima
   b. Buenos Aires
   c. Bogotá

3. Los pasajeros del vuelo 701 de Avianca pueden abordar el avión a las _____.
   a. ocho y cuarto
   b. ocho menos cuarto
   c. dos

4. El vuelo que sale de la puerta número doce va a _____.
   a. Buenos Aires
   b. Lima
   c. Bogotá

Palabras 2

E **¿Qué es or quién es?** Write the name of each place or person.

1. _____   2. _____   3. _____

4. _____   5. _____

F **Palabras derivadas.** Match each verb in the left column with the corresponding noun(s) in the right column.

1. _____ asistir   **a.** el vuelo
2. _____ reclamar   **b.** el aterrizaje
3. _____ controlar   **c.** el despegue
4. _____ volar   **d.** el control
5. _____ inspeccionar   **e.** el asistente, la asistenta
6. _____ despegar   **f.** la inspección
7. _____ aterrizar   **g.** el reclamo
8. _____ llegar   **h.** la llegada

G **Diccionario.** Give the word being defined.

1. el que trabaja a bordo del avión; sirve a los pasajeros _____

2. todo el personal a bordo de un avión _____

3. el comandante _____

4. los que viajan en el avión _____

5. el lugar donde inspeccionan o verifican los pasaportes _____

6. el lugar donde inspeccionan el equipaje de los pasajeros que llegan _____

ESTRUCTURA

El presente de los verbos hacer, poner, traer, salir *y* venir

A **Un viaje.** Form sentences using the expression *hacer un viaje.*

1. Yo / a España

   _____

2. Yo / con mi primo

   _____

3. Nosotros / en avión

   _____

4. Mis hermanos no / a España

   _____

5. Ellos / a México

   _____

6. ¿Adónde / sus padres?

   _____

7. Mis padres / a México también

   _____

B **Haciendo la maleta.** Complete each sentence with the correct form of *hacer, poner,* and *salir.*

1. Juan _____ la maleta. Él _____ una camisa en la maleta. Él _____ para Málaga.

2. Nosotros _____ nuestra maleta. Nosotros _____ blue jeans en la maleta. Nosotros _____ la maleta porque _____ para Cancún, México.

3. ¿Tú _____ tu maleta? ¿Para dónde _____?

4. Mis padres _____ su maleta. Ellos _____ muchas cosas en la maleta. Ellos _____ su maleta porque _____ para Miami.

5. Yo _____ mi maleta. Yo _____ blue jeans y T shirts en mi maleta. Yo _____ la maleta porque _____ para la Sierra de Guadarrama donde voy de camping.

C **Todos tenemos suerte.** These people are lucky because they are coming from a place they enjoyed a great deal. Complete each sentence with the correct form of *tener* and *venir*.

1. Yo _____ mucha suerte porque _____ de Toldeo, una ciudad fantástica cerca de Madrid.

2. Jesús y Juanita _____ mucha suerte porque _____ de Puerto Rico, una isla tropical en el mar Caribe que _____ playas estupendas.

3. Nosotros _____ mucha suerte porque _____ de la Ciudad de México, la fabulosa capital de nuestro país.

4. Jorge _____ mucha suerte porque _____ de Quito, una ciudad colonial en los Andes.

5. Tú también _____ mucha suerte porque _____ de Acapulco.

El presente progresivo

D **Un poco de gramática.** Give the present participle of each of the following verbs.

1. volar _____   4. hacer _____

2. llegar _____   5. salir _____

3. comer _____   6. leer _____

E **¿Qué están haciendo?** Rewrite each sentence using the present progressive tense.

1. Los pasajeros embarcan.

_____

2. El asistente de vuelo mira (revisa) las tarjetas de embarque.

_____

3. Los pasajeros buscan su asiento.

_____

4. Ponen su equipaje de mano en el compartimiento sobre su asiento.

_____

5. La asistenta de vuelo anuncia la salida.

_____

6. El avión despega.

_____

F **Un viaje.** Complete each sentence with the present progressive of the indicated verb(s).

1. Nosotros _____ un viaje. (hacer)

2. En este momento, nosotros _____ a una altura de 10.000 metros pero

   el avión todavía _____. (volar, subir)

3. Nosotros _____ los Andes. (sobrevolar)

4. Ahora el avión _____. (aterrizar)

5. Nosotros _____ al aeropuerto Jorge Chávez en Lima. (llegar)

G **¿Qué hacen ahora?** Answer the questions according to the illustrations.

1. ¿Qué están haciendo Teresa y Cristóbal ahora?

   _____

   _____

2. ¿Qué está haciendo el señor Aparicio ahora?

   _____

   _____

3. ¿Qué estoy haciendo ahora?

   _____

   _____

4. ¿Qué estamos haciendo ahora?

   _____

   _____

Nombre _____ Fecha _____

UN POCO MÁS

A **El boleto.** Here is an airline ticket. Fill it in using your own name. Make up your own trip.

aeroméxico	Origen		Destino	
Nombre de pasajero				
De	Transportador	Vuelo y Clase	Fecha	Hora
A				
Pasaje	Total		aeroméxico	
Impuestos				

B **El viaje.** Answer the following questions according to your airline ticket.

1. ¿Adónde vas?

   _____

2. ¿En qué vuelo sales?

   _____

3. ¿A qué hora sale tu vuelo?

   _____

4. ¿Qué día sales?

   _____

5. ¿Qué día vuelves?

   _____

6. ¿Cuál es el precio del boleto?

   _____

7. ¿Cuál es la línea aérea?

   _____

C ¡A viajar! Read the following ad that appeared in a travel brochure.

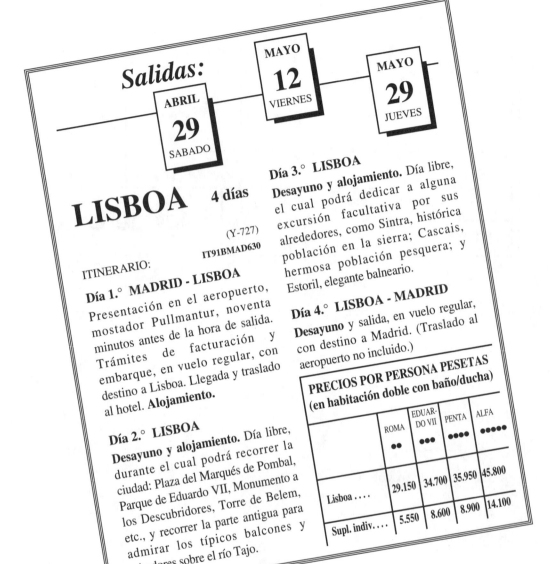

D **Adivinen.** Give the following expressions in Spanish.

1. transfer to hotel _____

2. free day _____

3. fishing village _____

4. elegant beach resort _____

5. price per person _____

E **Una tarjeta postal.** Pretend you are in the airport and you are taking a trip. Tell your friend where you are going, what you have to do at the airport, and what time your flight is leaving.

F **Las lenguas romances.** Spanish shares a lot of vocabulary with the other Romance languages derived from Latin. Look at the expressions below in Spanish, French, Italian, and Portuguese. Notice how much you could understand at an airport in Paris, Rome, Lisbon, or Rio de Janeiro.

Español	Francés	Italiano	Portugués
la línea aérea	la ligne aérienne	la linea aerea	a linha aérea
el vuelo	le vol	il vuolo	o vôo
el pasaporte	le passeport	il passaporto	o passaporte
la puerta	la porte	la porta	a porta
la tarjeta de embarque	la carte d'embarquement	la carta d'imbarco	a cartão de embarque
la aduana	la douane	la dogana	a alfândega
el destino	la destination	la destinazione	o destino
el billete (boleto)	le billet	il biglietto	o bilhete
el pasajero	le passager	il passaggero	o passageiro
el viaje	le voyage	il viaggio	a viagem

Read the following announcements in Spanish, French, and Italian. Do you think you would have any trouble understanding them if you were at an airport in Spain, France, or Italy?

Español
   Iberia anuncia la salida de su vuelo ciento cinco con destino a Madrid. Embarque inmediato por la puerta número siete, por favor.

Francés
   Air France annonce le départ de son vol cent cinq à destination de Paris. Embarquement immédiat par la porte numéro sept, s'il vous plaît.

Italiano
   Alitalia anuncia la partenza del vuolo cento cinque a destinazione Roma. Imbarco immediato per la porta numero sette, per favore.

MI AUTOBIOGRAFÍA

Do you like to travel? Do you travel often? Do you travel by plane? If you do, tell about your experiences. If you do not travel by plane, imagine a trip that you would like to take. Tell something about the airport near your home and something about the flight you are going to take. Include as many details as you can.

mi autobiografía

SELF-TEST 2

A Complete each sentence with the appropriate word(s).

1. Tres cuartos de una casa son _____ , _____ y
   _____ .

2. La familia vive en una _____ particular, no en un apartamento.

3. Ellos viven en la _____ Main.

4. María _____ un sándwich y _____ una limonada.

5. Yo leo el _____ y escribo con un _____ .

6. En el _____ hay árboles y _____ .

7. Yo tengo una bicicleta y mis padres tienen un _____ en el garaje.

8. El fútbol y el béisbol son _____ .

9. Juegan al fútbol en el _____ de fútbol.

10. Si el _____ no puede parar el balón y entra en la portería, el otro
    _____ mete un gol y marca un _____ .

B Tell which of your relatives is being described.

1. el otro hijo de mis padres _____

2. la madre de mi padre _____

3. el hermano de mi padre _____

4. el hijo de la hermana de mi padre _____

C Write the name of each item or person.

1. _____   2. _____   3. _____

4. _____   5. _____

D Complete each sentence with the correct form of the indicated verb.

1. Yo _____ la televisión en la sala. (ver)

2. Nosotros _____ en el comedor. (comer)

3. Nosotros _____ en una casa particular. (vivir)

4. Yo _____ notas muy buenas en la escuela. (recibir)

5. Ellos _____ mucho. (leer)

6. Yo _____ una familia grande. (tener)

7. Nosotros _____ un perro. (tener)

8. Mi tía _____ tres hijos. (tener)

9. Yo _____ un viaje. (hacer)

10. El taxista _____ las maletas en la maletera del taxi. (poner)

11. Yo _____ para el aeropuerto. (salir)

12. Nosotros _____ para Madrid. (salir)

E Rewrite each sentence changing the singular to the plural or vice versa.

1. Yo empiezo ahora.

   Nosotros _____

2. Él quiere salir.

   Ellos _____

3. ¿Tú puedes?

   ¿Uds. _____

4. Ellos juegan bien.

   Él _____

5. Yo vuelvo ahora.

   Nosotros _____

6. Yo prefiero comer ahora.

   Nosotros _____

7. Ellas duermen ocho horas.

   Ella _____

F Complete each sentence with correct form of the possessive adjective(s).

1. Yo tengo una hermana. _____ hermana tiene once años.

2. El libro es de Juan. _____ libro es muy interesante.

3. Nosotros vivimos en los suburbios. _____ casa tiene un jardín.

4. Mi tío es muy simpático. _____ hijos son _____ primos.

5. Si vas a hacer un viaje, ¿tienes _____ billetes y _____ pasaporte?

G Rewrite each sentence using the present progressive tense.

1. Ellos salen ahora.

   _____

2. Hago el viaje con ellos.

   _____

3. Viajamos en avión.

   _____

4. Yo leo y él escribe.

   _____

5. Los pasajeros ponen su equipaje en el compartimiento.

   _____

6. Tú reclamas las maletas.

   _____

H Complete each sentence with *hay, tener que,* or *ir a.*

1. _____ muchos alumnos en nuestra clase de español.

2. Yo _____ estudiar mucho si quiero recibir buenas notas.

3. Mañana nosotros _____ tener un examen. Nosotros
   _____ estudiar para el examen.

4. Elena y Paco _____ ir a la tienda de discos. Ellos _____
   comprar un regalo para su prima, Teresa. Teresa _____ cumplir los quince
   años el martes.

I Tell whether each statement is true or false.

1. _____ En Latinoamérica no hay suburbios.

2. _____ En Latinoamérica mucha gente vive en apartamentos en el centro de las ciudades.

3. _____ Una señora hispana tiene (lleva) el apellido de su familia y también el apellido de la familia de su esposo.

4. _____ El fútbol (soccer) es el deporte más popular en España y Latinoamérica.

5. _____ El fútbol que juegan en España y en Latinoamérica es el mismo fútbol que juegan en los Estados Unidos.

6. _____ El avión no es muy importante en la América del Sur.

7. _____ Los Andes son montañas muy altas.

8. _____ Es fácil viajar por tierra por las selvas tropicales de la América del Sur.

Answers appear on pages 178–179.

CAPÍTULO

9

DEPORTES Y ACTIVIDADES
DE INVIERNO

VOCABULARIO

Palabras 1

A **¿Qué es?** Write the name of each item.

1. _____   2. _____   3. _____

4. _____   5. _____   6. _____

B **Palabras derivadas.** Match each verb in the left column with the corresponding noun(s) in the right column.

1. _____ subir   **a.** el esquí
2. _____ bajar   **b.** la nieve, la nevada
3. _____ descender   **c.** la bajada
4. _____ esquiar   **d.** la subida
5. _____ nevar   **e.** el descenso

C ¡A esquiar! Complete each sentence with an appropriate word.

1. El esquiador _____ en el telesilla, no baja.

2. Los esquiadores llevan _____ como protección del reflejo del sol en la nieve.

3. Él no es experto. Es _____. Es solamente la segunda o tercera vez que esquía.

4. Hoy está nevando mucho. Hay mucha _____.

5. Él exagera un poco. Es un poco _____.

D El equipo necesario. Make a list of necessary ski equipment.

1. _____   4. _____

2. _____   5. _____

3. _____   6. _____

Palabras 2

E ¿Qué es? Write the name of each item.

1. _____   2. _____

3. _____   4. _____

F   **El patinaje.** Complete each sentence with an appropriate word.

1. Una pista al aire libre no tiene techo pero una pista _____ sí, tiene techo.

2. Los patines para el patinaje sobre hielo tienen _____.

3. Los patinadores bailan cuando hacen el _____.

4. Hay pistas cubiertas y pistas _____ donde patina la gente sobre hielo.

G   **Lo contrario.** Write the opposite.

1. Estos patines tienen cuchilla (hoja).

   _____

2. Estos patines tienen ruedas.

   _____

3. Es una pista al aire libre.

   _____

4. Están haciendo el patinaje sobre hielo.

   _____

H   **¿Sí o no?** Tell whether each statement is true or false according to the illustration.

1. _____   Es el patinaje sobre hielo.
2. _____   Es una pista cubierta.
3. _____   Es una pista para el patinaje sobre ruedas.
4. _____   Los patines tienen ruedas.
5. _____   Los patinadores llevan gafas.
6. _____   Hay mucha nieve en la pista.
7. _____   Los dos patinadores llevan guantes.

ESTRUCTURA

El presente de los verbos saber y conocer

A   **Lo que sé hacer.** In complete sentences, write five things you know how to do.

1. _____

2. _____

3. _____

4. _____

5. _____

B   **¿A quiénes conoces?** In complete sentences, write the names of five people you know.

1. _____

2. _____

3. _____

4. _____

5. _____

C   **Un(a) buen(a) amigo(a).** Write a paragraph about a good friend. In the paragraph, answer the following questions: *¿Sabes su número de teléfono? ¿Cuál es? ¿Conoce él o ella a toda tu familia? ¿Conoces a toda su familia también? ¿Cuáles son algunas cosas que él o ella sabe hacer muy bien? ¿Sabes hacer las mismas cosas?*

_____

_____

_____

_____

_____

_____

_____

_____

_____

D **Un viaje a Puerto Rico.** Complete each sentence with the correct form of *saber* or *conocer.*

1. Miguel _____ que mañana va a salir para San Juan.

2. Él _____ el número de su vuelo y a qué hora va a salir.

3. Como Miguel es de Puerto Rico, él _____ a mucha gente en la isla.

4. Él _____ la historia de Puerto Rico también.

5. Él _____ que no tiene que llevar pasaporte a Puerto Rico.

6. Él _____ que Puerto Rico es un estado libre asociado de los Estados Unidos.

E **¿Saber o conocer?** Form sentences using *saber* or *conocer.*

1. Yo / a la instructora

   _____

2. Ella / esquiar muy bien

   _____

3. Ella / enseñar bien

   _____

4. Ella / a todos sus alumnos

   _____

5. Yo / que ella es argentina

   _____

El presente del verbo decir

F **¿Qué dices?** Complete each sentence with the correct form of *decir.*

1. Yo _____ que un colegio en Latinoamérica es una escuela superior en los Estados Unidos.

2. Nosotros siempre _____ que un amigo sincero es un tesoro.

3. Ellos _____ que mucha gente de la clase media vive en apartamentos en el centro de las grandes ciudades.

4. ¿_____ tú que hay estaciones de esquí famosas en los Andes?

5. ¿_____ Uds. que en su país muchos alumnos asisten a escuelas privadas?

6. Yo _____ que en nuestra escuela el deporte más popular es el fútbol.

7. Nosotros _____ que este año vamos a aprender a esquiar.

G **¿Dice que sí o que no?** Answer the following questions.

1. ¿Dice Paco que es esquiador experto?

   _____

2. ¿Dicen los patinadores principiantes que saben hacer el patinaje artístico?

   _____

3. ¿Dicen Uds. que prefieren el invierno?

   _____

4. ¿Dices tú que eres un poco fanfarrón (fanfarrona)?

   _____

Los adjetivos demostrativos

H **En el aeropuerto.** Complete the sentences with the correct form of *este*, *ese*, or *aquel*.

1. El avión que sale de _____ puerta aquí va a San Juan. El avión que sale de

   _____ puerta allá va a Miami.

2. _____ avión que va a San Juan es un A300. _____ avión

   que va a Miami es un 727.

3. _____ pasajeros que hacen cola (fila) aquí van a San Juan.

4. _____ pasajeros que esperan allá en _____ puerta van a Miami.

5. _____ vuelo (a San Juan) sale antes que _____ vuelo.

I **El equipaje.** Complete the conversation with the correct form of *este*, *ese*, or *aquel*.

—Chefa, _____ maleta que yo tengo es pequeña. Pero _____
                           1   2

  maleta que tú llevas es grandísima (muy grande).

—¿Tú dices que _____ maleta que yo tengo es grande? ¿Ves
                                  3

  _____ maleta allá?
              4

—¿De qué maleta estás hablando?

—De la maleta que lleva _____ señora allá en el mostrador.
                                   5

—¡Es verdad! _____ maleta que tú tienes es pequeña comparada con la
                  6

  maleta que lleva _____ señora.
                   7

UN POCO MÁS

A **¡A esquiar!** Read the following advertisement from an Argentine newspaper. In a word or two, answer each question according to the ad.

1. What is the name of the travel agency?

_____

2. How many types of excursions does the travel agency offer?

_____

3. Is it necessary to have one's own equipment in order to book a trip?

_____

4. Are there trips for beginners as well as experts?

_____

5. Is there only one departure each week?

_____

6. How many departures are there each week?

_____

7. When do the departures begin?

_____

8. When do the departures end?

_____

9. Which ski resort do these trips go to?

_____

10. In what country is Portillo?

_____

11. The prices shown are for how many days?

_____

ESQUÍ

A NIVEL *Cavaliere*

Cavaliere, el operador turístico de nivel internacional

CUATRO CATEGORÍAS

- **Expertos con equipo**
  Incluye profesor de su nivel y provisión de equipo
- **Expertos**
  Igual cobertura, sin la provisión de equipo
- **Futuros**
  Provisión de equipo completo y dos clases diarias con profesor exclusivo para grupos reducidos
- **Niños con escuela de esquí**
  Niños de 3 a 11 años que pasan el día entero a cargo de personal especializado y aprenden jugando. Se incluye pensión completa y provisión de equipo.

CUATRO SALIDAS SEMANALES

Martes, Jueves, Sábados y Domingos
desde el 19 de junio hasta el 23 de octubre

Portillo — 8 días

Expertos c/ equipo	de 39.980 a 52.000
Expertos	de 3l.700 a 51.500
Futuros	de 40.680 a 54.900
Niños / escuela	de 32.900 a 48.300

Cavaliere

lo prometido… y más.
Córdoba 617 primer piso • Res. 658 • 74

MI AUTOBIOGRAFÍA

What is the weather like in your town in the winter? Do you live near the mountains or not? Do you prefer one of the other seasons rather than winter? Tell whether or not you participate in winter sports such as skating or skiing. If you do, tell about your experiences. If you do not, what is your opinion of skating and skiing? Do you think you would like to try them? If not, tell what you prefer to do.

mi autobiografía

CAPÍTULO 10

LA SALUD Y EL MÉDICO

VOCABULARIO

Palabras 1

A **¿Cómo está la persona?** Describe each person's condition according to the illustration.

1. _____   2. _____   3. _____

4. _____   5. _____

B **Síntomas.** Decide what the illness is.

	la gripe	un catarro	los dos
1. Está estornando mucho.	_____	_____	_____
2. Tiene fiebre.	_____	_____	_____
3. Tiene dolor de cabeza.	_____	_____	_____
4. Tiene tos.	_____	_____	_____
5. Tiene escalofríos.	_____	_____	_____

C **¿Cómo está?** Complete each sentence with an appropriate word.

1. Ella está _____ porque sabe que va a recibir una nota muy buena.
2. Ella está _____ y quiere dormir.
3. Ella está _____. Tiene dolor de garganta.
4. Ella está _____ porque no sabe si su hermano está muy enfermo o no.

Palabras 2

D **La medicina.** Complete each sentence with the appropriate word(s).

1. El médico examina a sus pacientes en el _____ o en la

   _____.
2. El _____ o la _____ ayuda al médico.
3. Yo abro la boca cuando el médico me examina la _____.
4. El médico me da una _____ para antibióticos.
5. Los medicamentos vienen en forma de _____ o _____.
6. El / La farmacéutico(a) trabaja en la _____.
7. El / La farmacéutico(a) _____ los medicamentos.

E **¡Cuánto me duele!** Tell where it hurts, according to the illustrations. Use *me duele*.

1. _____

   _____

2. _____

   _____

3. _____

   _____

4. _____

   _____

F **El enfermo.** Answer the questions according to the illustration.

1. ¿Está el paciente en el hospital?

   _____

2. ¿Dónde está?

   _____

3. ¿Está en cama o no?

   _____

4. ¿Con quién habla el paciente?

   _____

G **En el consultorio.** Write sentences telling what the doctor does to you.

1. decir "buenos días" _____

2. preguntar qué tengo _____

3. examinar _____

4. recetar unos medicamentos _____

5. dar la receta _____

6. explicar la diagnosis _____

ESTRUCTURA

Ser y estar

A **Josefa.** Write sentences about Josefa according to the illustrations. Use *ser* and *estar*.

1. _____

   _____

2. _____

   _____

3. _____

   _____

4. _____

   _____

B **¿Cómo es? ¿Cómo está?** Form sentences using *ser* or *estar*.

1. María y Tómas / divertidos

   _____

2. Yo / muy aburrido(a) en mi clase de inglés

   _____

3. El curso de español / bastante difícil

   _____

4. Nosotras / cansadas

   _____

5. Tú / enferma

   _____

C **¿De dónde es? ¿Dónde está?** Look at the maps. The first map tells where the person is from. The second map tells where the person is right now. Write a sentence telling where the person is from and where he/she is now. Use *ser* and *estar*.

1. Yo _____

_____

2. Alberto y Lola _____

_____

3. Isabel _____

_____

 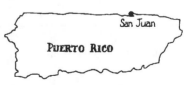

4. Nosotros _____

_____

D **¿Y tú?** Give your own answers.

1. ¿De dónde eres? ¿Dónde estás ahora?

_____

_____

2. Tu mamá o tu papá, ¿de dónde es? ¿Dónde está ahora?

_____

_____

E **La médica.** Complete with the correct forms of *ser* or *estar.*

La médica _____ muy inteligente. Ella _____ de
    1   2

Nicaragua. _____ nicaragüense. Ella _____ especialista
              3   4

en cirugía. _____ cirujana. Muchos de sus pacientes _____
               5   6

muy enfermos. Pero la doctora García _____ muy simpática. Ella
                                          7

_____ muy amable con sus pacientes. Su consultorio _____
      8   9

en el hospital mismo. _____ en la planta baja del hospital. La sala de
                         10

operaciones _____ en el mismo edificio que su consultorio.
               11

Los pronombres me, te, nos

F **Al médico.** Answer the following questions.

1. Si estás enfermo(a), ¿te examina el médico?

_____

2. ¿Te hace la diagnosis?

_____

3. Si tienes dolor de garganta, ¿te receta unas pastillas el médico?

_____

4. Carlos, ¿me va a dar una inyección?

_____

UN POCO MÁS

A **Un problema médico.** Read the following article that appeared in *Blanco y Negro*, a magazine in Madrid.

> **Las emociones como enojo, miedo o ansiedad también pueden hacer subir la presión arterial, aprenda a relajarse**
>
> La hipertensión es un problema que nos puede afectar a todos. Cada día en nuestro país, 7.000.000 de personas se enfrentan con el problema de la hipertensión. En general llevan una vida prácticamente normal, evitando los excesos. La fatiga, la ansiedad y las tensiones emocionales, a las que muchas veces nos conduce el estilo de la vida moderna, inciden de forma negativa sobre el organismo, particularmente sobre el del hipertenso, porque puede provocar bruscas (rápidas) alteraciones de la tensión arterial.

B **La tensión arterial.** Complete each sentence according to the article.

1. Este artículo habla del problema de la _____.

2. En España _____ de personas sufren de hipertensión.

3. Las víctimas de la hipertensión tienen una vida casi _____.

4. Pero es necesario evitar los _____.

5. Tres factores con consecuencias negativas para la persona con hipertensión son la
   _____, la _____ y la _____.

6. Estos factores pueden causar alteraciones de la _____.

C **Los primeros auxilios.** Read the following article that appeared recently in *Vanidades.*

Notas

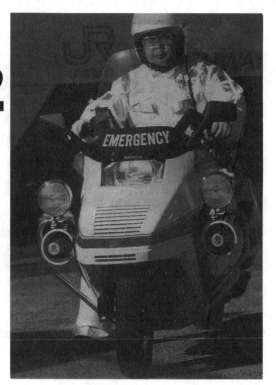

¿Está al tanto de los últimos inventos?

¡Ambulancias en moto y sillas de azúcar!

LA MEDICINA SE MOTORIZA EN JAPON
El médico llega en motoambulancia

Este invento japonés sirve para reducir el tiempo que le toma a una ambulancia internarse en el tráfico de una ciudad para llegar al lugar donde una persona lesionada requiere primeros auxilios. Conducida por un médico, la motoambulancia Honda contiene un aparato de electrocardiograma, máscara de oxígeno y 50 artículos más, necesarios para dar los primeros auxilios. Debido a su tamaño, puede deslizarse entre los autos a toda velocidad.

En estos momentos hay dos de prueba circulando por las calles de Tokio. Los médicos que las conducen son expertos motociclistas. Aunque no... no dan consultas a los automovilistas en medio del tráfico.

D **El invento.** Choose the word or expression that correctly answers each question.

1. ¿De qué trata este artículo?
   a. de un accidente
   b. de una motoambulancia
   c. de un médico japonés

2. ¿Quiénes inventaron este aparato?
   a. los americanos
   b. los médicos
   c. los japoneses

3. ¿Cómo es la motoambulancia?
   a. pequeña
   b. enorme
   c. grande

4. ¿Cuántas motoambulancias hay en Tokio?
   a. no hay ninguna
   b. hay muchas
   c. sólo hay dos

E **Adivinen.** Figure out the meaning of each of the following.

1. los primeros auxilios _____

2. un aparato de electrocardiograma _____

3. deslizarse entre los autos _____

F **Empleo.** Look at the following employment ad that appeared in a San Juan newspaper.

HOSPITAL SAN CARLOS BORROMEO

SOLICITA
ENFERMERAS (OS) GRADUADAS(OS)

Requisitos:
- Licencia provisional o permanente
- Bachillerato o Asociado en Ciencias de Enfermería
- Disponibilidad para turnos rotativos
- Curso de Intensivo

TECNICOS (AS) DE TERAPIA RESPIRATORIA

Requisitos:
- Licencia provisional o permanente
- Disponibilidad para hacer turnos
- Preferiblemente con experiencia

TECNICA DE TRANSCRIPCION

Requisitos:
- Conocimiento de términos médicos de radiología
- Total dominio del inglés
- Maquinilla preferiblemente 1 año de experiencia.

Ofrecemos competentes salarios y amplios beneficios marginales.

Los interesados, favor llamar al **877-8000 ext. 282,** pasar por la Oficina de Personal del Hospital San Carlos o enviar resumé a la siguiente dirección:
**Hospital San Carlos Borromeo
BOX 68, Moca, P. R. 00676**

"Patrono con igualdad de oportunidades de empleo"

G **Los informes.** Give the following information according to the ad.

1. el nombre del hospital _____

2. donde está el hospital _____

3. qué busca (solicita, necesita) el hospital _____
_____

H **Expresiones.** Give the Spanish equivalent for each of the following expressions, according to the ad.

1. equal opportunity employer _____

2. good fringe benefits _____

3. complete mastery of English _____

4. rotating shifts _____

MI AUTOBIOGRAFÍA

Tell some things about yourself. What makes you happy? What makes you sad? What do you do when you do not feel well? What is the name of your family doctor? Where is his/her office? How often do you see the doctor? Write about some of the minor ailments you get once in a while. Are you a good patient or not? You may want to ask a family member.

mi autobiografía

CAPÍTULO

11

ACTIVIDADES DE VERANO

VOCABULARIO

Palabras 1

A **¿Qué es?** Write the name of each item.

1. _____

2. _____

3. _____

4. _____

5. _____

6. _____

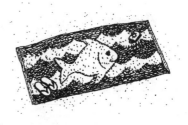

7. _____

8. _____

B **Un día en la playa.** Write sentences telling what Gloria and her friends did on the beach yesterday. Use the illustration as a guide.

1. _____
2. _____
3. _____
4. _____
5. _____

C **El tiempo en el verano.** Look at the illustration again in Exercise B. Describe the weather.

_____
_____
_____
_____

Nombre _____ Fecha _____

D **Una tarjeta postal.** Read Eduardo's postcard. Then answer the questions that follow.

Queridos amigos,
Aquí estoy en la playa de Marbella. Marbella es un pueblo bonito en la Costa del Sol, en el sur de España. El mar aquí, el Mediterráneo, siempre está en calma en el verano. A veces hay algunas olas pequeñas. Todos los días hace buen tiempo. Siempre uso una crema protectora y pongo mi silla debajo de una sombrilla. ¡Qué contento estoy aquí! Saludos,
Eduardo

La Familia Salas
Calle Sol, Nº 4
San Juan, PR 00926

1. ¿Dónde está Eduardo?
   en la Playa

2. ¿Dónde está Marbella?
   un Pueblo

3. ¿Marbella está en la costa de qué mar?
   Si

4. ¿Cómo está el mar Mediterráneo, sobre todo en el verano?
   Si

5. A veces, ¿qué hay en el mar?
   alughas olas Pequetos

6. ¿Qué usa Eduardo?
   eduardo es escribe

7. ¿Dónde pone su silla Eduardo?
   sombrilla

Palabras 2

E **Actividades de verano.** Complete each sentence with the appropriate word(s).

1. Es posible nadar en la _____, en el _____ o en el
   _____.

2. Para jugar al tenis, es necesario tener una _____.

3. Los jugadores juegan al tenis en la _____ de tenis.

4. Dos partes de una raqueta son el _____ y la _____.

5. El jugador o la jugadora de golf pone sus palos en la _____ de golf.

6. Juegan (al) golf en el _____ de golf.

7. La _____ tiene que entrar en el hoyo.

8. El hoyo está en el _____.

F **Lo que necesito.** For each place illustrated, you need certain things. Make a list of what you need for each place.

1. _____
   _____
   _____
   _____

2. _____
   _____
   _____
   _____

3. _____
   _____
   _____
   _____

ESTRUCTURA

El pretérito de los verbos en –ar

A **El verano.** Complete each sentence with the correct preterite forms of the indicated verb.

1. Él _____ en el mar y yo _____ en el lago. (esquiar)
2. Ella _____ en el lago y yo _____ en la piscina. (nadar)
3. Él _____ un barquito y yo _____ una sombrilla. (alquilar)
4. Ella _____ el día en la playa y yo _____ el día en casa. (pasar)

B **De compras.** Complete with the correct preterite forms of the indicated verbs.

—¿Qué _____ tú? (comprar)
          1

— _____ una raqueta. (comprar)
    2

—¿Dónde la _____? (comprar)
       3

—La _____ en una tienda en el centro comercial. (comprar)
    4

—¿Cuánto _____? (pagar)
      5

— _____ cinco mil pesos. (pagar)
    6

C **Una visita al museo.** Rewrite each sentence in the plural.

1. Visitó el museo del Prado.

   _____

2. Compró billetes reducidos para estudiantes.

   _____

3. Entró en el museo.

   _____

4. Miró los cuadros de Goya, Velázquez, El Greco y Murillo. Admiró *Las Meninas* de Velázquez.

   _____

   _____

5. Pasó unas tres horas en el museo.

   _____

D **¿Y Uds.?** Complete each sentence with the correct form of the indicated verb.

1. (llegar)

   Ayer nosotros _____ a la escuela a las ocho.

   ¿A qué hora _____ Uds.?

2. (hablar)

   Ayer nosotros _____ con la profesora de español.

   ¿Con quién _____ Uds.?

3. (tomar)

   Nosotros _____ un examen.

   ¿En qué clase lo _____ Uds.?

4. (tomar)

   Nosotros _____ el almuerzo en la cafetería.

   ¿Dónde lo _____ Uds.?

5. (jugar)

   Después de las clases, nosotros _____ al tenis.

   ¿Cuándo _____ Uds.?

6. (pagar)

   Nosotros _____ 150 pesos para alquilar la sombrilla.

   ¿Cuánto _____ Uds.?

E **Un día en la playa de Marbella.** Complete each sentence with the correct preterite verb ending.

1. Anita tom_____ el sol.
2. José Luis nad_____.
3. Yo esqui_____ en el agua.
4. Maripaz y Nando buce_____.
5. Y luego todos nosotros tom_____ un refresco en un café.
6. Yo tom_____ una limonada.
7. Anita tom_____ un helado.
8. ¿Y quién pag_____? Anita pag_____.
9. Y tú, ¿pas_____ el día en la playa con tus amigos?
10. ¿No? ¿Uds. no pas_____ el día en la playa? ¡Qué pena!

F ¡Cuidado! Complete each sentence with the correct preterite forms of the indicated verb.

1. Yo _____ la guitarra y él la _____ también. (tocar)
2. Yo _____ y ella _____ también. (jugar)
3. Yo _____ y él _____ a la misma hora. (llegar)
4. Yo _____ un tanto y ella _____ otro. (marcar)
5. Yo _____ y ella _____ también. (pagar)
6. Yo _____ a las ocho y él _____ a las nueve. (empezar)
7. Yo _____ una silla y él _____ una silla también. (buscar)

Los pronombres de complemento directo

G **La playa.** Rewrite each sentence substituting *lo, la, los,* or *las* for the indicated direct object.

1. Teresa compró *la crema protectora.*

   _____

2. Ella usó *la crema protectora* en la playa.

   _____

3. Carlos tiene un nuevo bañador. Él compró *el bañador* ayer.

   _____

4. Los amigos de Carlos y Teresa pasaron un día muy agradable. Pasaron *el día* en la playa.

   _____

   _____

5. Ellos esquiaron en el agua. Alquilaron *los esquís* en la playa.

   _____

6. Rafael usa anteojos de sol. Compró *los anteojos de sol* ayer.

   _____

7. Yo tomé fotos instantáneas. Tomé *las fotos* en la playa.

   _____

8. Carmen miró *las fotos.*

   _____

H ¿**Adónde vas?** Answer each question. Use object pronouns when possible.

1. ¿Tienes la raqueta? _____

   ¿Adónde vas? _____

2. ¿Tienes tus bastones? _____

   ¿Tienes tus bolas? _____

   ¿A qué vas a jugar? _____

3. ¿Tienes tu bañador? _____

   ¿Qué vas a hacer? _____

4. ¿Tienes la pelota? _____

   ¿Tienes el bate? _____

   ¿Tienes el guante? _____

   ¿A qué vas a jugar? _____

5. ¿Tienes los esquís? _____

   ¿Tienes los bastones? _____

   ¿Tienes tus guantes? _____

   ¿Tienes tus botas? _____

   ¿Qué vas a hacer? _____

El pretérito de los verbos ir y ser

I ¡**Ayer!** Complete each sentence with the correct preterite forms of *ir*.

1. Yo _____ a la escuela y él también _____.
2. Yo _____ al mercado y él también _____.
3. Yo _____ a la playa y él también _____.
4. Yo _____ al lago y él también _____.
5. Nosotros _____ a la piscina y ellos también _____.
6. Nosotros _____ al campo de golf y ellos también _____.
7. Nosotros _____ a patinar y ellos también _____.

UN POCO MÁS

A **Protección.** Read the following advice that appeared in the magazine *Medix*.

> ### LAS GAFAS PARA EL SOL:
>
> ## ¿SABE USTED CUÁL ES POR ALEX PEREIRA LA **PROTECCIÓN** EXACTA QUE NECESITAN SUS **OJOS**?
>
> No todas las *gafas* o *anteojos para el sol* protegen igualmente sus ojos... Existen algunos que ni siquiera le ofrecen protección. ¡Aprenda a seleccionar correctamente cuáles son los que sus ojos necesitan!

B **Aviso.** What advice is offered in the notice you just read?

_____

_____

C **Palabras derivadas.** Match each verb in the left column with the corresponding noun in the right column.

1. _____ proteger   **a.** la necesidad
2. _____ necesitar   **b.** la selección
3. _____ existir   **c.** la protección
4. _____ seleccionar   **d.** la existencia

Nombre _____ Fecha _____

D **El tenis.** Read the following article that appeared in the magazine *Vanidades*.

El origen del tenis

La palabra "tenis" — aplicada al popular deporte—
viene del árabe "tenetz", una adaptación de la
palabra "tenez", que significa "saltar". Y la palabra
"raqueta" también viene del árabe, ya que "rahet"
significa "en la palma de la mano" y cuando el
deporte se inició, los jugadores le daban a la pelota
usando la palma de la mano... en vez de utilizar una
raqueta, como en nuestros días.

E **Preguntas.** In a word or two, answer the following questions according to the article in Exercise D.

1. ¿Qué es el tenis?

   _____

2. ¿De qué lengua viene la palabra "tenis"?

   _____

3. ¿Viene la palabra "raqueta" de la misma lengua?

   _____

4. Hoy, ¿usan los tenistas la palma de la mano para darle a la pelota?

   _____

5. En vez de usar la palma de la mano, ¿qué usan?

   _____

F **¿Qué quiere decir?** Give the meaning of each of the following words.

1. rahet _____

2. tenetz _____

G **Una atleta.** Read the following article that appeared in the magazine *Más*.

> **M**ary Joe Fernández, de 20 anos, nacío en la República Dominicana y es hija de cubana y español. Clasificada entre las siete mejores del mundo, representará a EE UU en sencillos, junto con Jennifer Capriati y Zina Garrison, y será pareja de Gigi Fernández en dobles. Su figura fina engaña. Posee una derecha potente y ha ganado más de $1.9 millones. El futuro la verá desarrollarse de forma aún más impresionante.

H **Mary Joe Fernández.** Complete each sentence according to the article in Exercise G.

1. El deporte de Mary Joe es el _____.

2. El padre de Mary Joe es de _____.

3. Ella va a jugar dobles con _____.

4. Ella recibió más de _____ de dólares en premios.

5. Mary Joe nació en la _____.

I **¿Dónde dice… ?** Find the word or expression in the article in Exercise G that means the same as each of the following.

1. que Mary Joe es una jugadora excelente

_____

2. cómo es el brazo de Mary Joe

_____

J **La natación.** Read the following article that appeared in the magazine *Más*.

MARTIN LOPEZ ZUBERO

La fiesta en la piscina Bernat Picornell tendrá sabor americano. Tan buenos son los nadadores de las Américas. Anita Nall, con 16 años, es la plusmarquista mundial en los 200 metros pecho y fácilmente puede robarse el espectáculo. Pero los sueños no conocen fronteras. Martín López Zubero, plusmarquista mundial en los 200 metros espalda, de madre americana y padre aragonés, es la medalla de oro más segura de España. El surinamés Anthony Nesty, campeón olímpico y mundial en los 100 metros, y primer nadador de raza negra en ganar medalla olímpica, representa las esperanzas suramericanas. El más completo de todos es el húngaro Tamas Darnyi. Tuerto del ojo izquierdo, lleva ocho años invicto en los 200 y 400 metros estilo.

K **El anuncio.** Choose the correct answer according to the article in Exercise J.

1. ¿Qué es Bernat Picornell?
   a. un nadador americano
   b. una piscina
   c. un aragonés

2. ¿Qué record tiene López Zubero?
   a. la medalla de oro
   b. 200 metros espalda
   c. España

3. ¿De dónde es la madre de López Zubero?
   a. los Estados Unidos
   b. Aragón
   c. España

4. ¿Cuántos años tiene Anita Nall?
   a. dieciséis
   b. veinte
   c. veinte y dos

L **Adivinen.** Figure it out or guess.

1. How do you say "backstroke?" _____
2. How do you say "record holder?" _____
3. How do you say "breaststroke?" _____

MI AUTOBIOGRAFÍA

Write about the summer weather where you live. Also, write about what you do in the summer. If you swim, tell where. Do you live near a beach? Do you participate in summer sports or do you prefer to be a spectator? Write as much as you can about your summer vacations *(vacaciones)* and your summer activities.

Mi autobiografía

CAPÍTULO

12

ACTIVIDADES CULTURALES

VOCABULARIO

Palabras 1

A **En la taquilla del cine.** Complete each sentence according to the illustration.

1. La gente está en la _____ para comprar entradas al _____.

2. Venden (Despachan) las _____ en la taquilla.

3. La gente que quiere entrar en el cine para ver una _____ hace una _____ delante de la taquilla.

4. La próxima _____ empieza a las 8:15.

5. Cerca del cine hay una estación de _____.

B **Lo mismo.** Match the word in the left column with a word that means the same in the right column.

1. _____ la taquilla   **a.** la localidad, el boleto, el billete

2. _____ la entrada   **b.** la silla, el asiento

3. _____ la película   **c.** la ventanilla, la boletería

4. _____ la butaca   **d.** la fila

5. _____ la cola   **e.** el film, el filme

Palabras 2

C **¿Qué es o quién es?** Write the name of each item or person.

1. _____

2. _____

3. _____

4. _____

5. _____

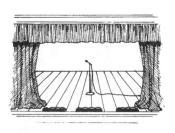

6. _____

7. _____

8. _____

D **El teatro o el cine.** Complete each sentence with the appropriate word(s).

1. En el cine hay una pantalla y en el teatro hay una _____.

2. En el cine presentan una película y en el teatro dan _____.

3. En el _____ los actores y las actrices entran en escena.

4. Los espectadores toman su _____ en el cine y también en el teatro.

5. Hay tres o más _____ en el cine en un día, pero en el

   _____ , no.

E **¿Quién?** Write the name of the person being described.

1. él hace (juega) el papel de un personaje en una obra teatral _____

2. ella hace (juega) el papel de un personaje en una obra teatral _____

3. él toca un instrumento musical en una orquesta _____

4. ella dirige la orquesta _____

5. ella hace estatuas _____

6. él pinta cuadros _____

7. él trabaja en un restaurante _____

F **¿Qué es o quién es?** Write the name of each item or person.

1. _____   2. _____   3. _____

4. _____   5. _____   6. _____

7. _____   8. _____

G **¿Sí o no?** Tell whether each statement is true or false.

1. _____ El mesero trabaja en un restaurante.
2. _____ Hay una exposición de arte en el cine.
3. _____ Ellos ven una película en la pantalla.
4. _____ Un carro es un medio de transporte.
5. _____ La mesera deja la propina después de la comida.
6. _____ La escultora dio una representación en el cine.
7. _____ Un menú es una lista de los platos (las comidas).
8. _____ Los músicos tocan instrumentos en una orquesta.
9. _____ Los espectadores aplauden después del espectáculo musical.
10. _____ Los artistas pintaron el mural.
11. _____ Antes de entrar en el teatro hay que comprar una taquilla.
12. _____ Vimos los cuadros de Velázquez en la pantalla.
13. _____ Un documental es un tipo de película.

H **Unas preguntas.** Make up a question about each statement. Use the indicated words as a guide.

1. Alejandra salió *anoche.*

   _____

2. Ella salió *con una amiga.*

   _____

3. Ellas vieron *una película* en el Cine Imperial.

   _____

4. Ellas pagaron *cuatro dólares* por las entradas.

   _____

5. Luego comieron *en un restaurante.*

   _____

6. Ellas comieron *muy bien.*

   _____

7. Volvieron a casa *a las diez y media de la noche.*

   _____

ESTRUCTURA

El pretérito de los verbos en –er e –ir

A **Una carta a un(a) amigo(a).** Write a friend a short letter. Tell him or her: you went out last night, you saw a good movie, you saw the movie at the *Cine Rex*, afterwards you ate at a restaurant, you returned home at 10:30.

B **Otra carta.** Rewrite the letter from Exercise A. Tell your friend what you and Guillermo did.

C **El entremetido.** Complete each sentence with the correct preterite form(s) of the indicated verb(s).

1. Carlos _____ anoche y no _____ hasta las once. (salir, volver)

2. Él y sus amigos _____ una película. (ver)

3. Ellos la _____ en inglés. (ver)

4. Carlos, ¿_____ (tú) la película que _____ en inglés? (comprender, ver)

5. ¡Oye, hombre! ¿Por qué me preguntas? Claro que yo la _____. (comprender)

6. No te quiero insultar. Pero, ¿tú _____ bastante inglés en la escuela para comprender una película americana? (aprender)

7. Pues, sí. Yo _____ mucho inglés. (aprender)

8. Yo _____ muy buenas notas en la clase de inglés. (recibir)

9. ¿A qué hora _____ Uds. del cine? (salir)

10. Pues, nosotros _____ a eso de las nueve y media. (salir)

11. Si Uds. _____ a las nueve y media, ¿por qué no _____ (tú) a casa hasta las once? (salir, volver)

12. Tú haces muchas preguntas, ¿sabes? Pero te voy a contestar. Todos nosotros _____ ir a comer algo en la cafetería Fénix. (decidir)

13. No te voy a preguntar lo que _____. (comer)

14. Y, ¿por qué no me preguntas con quien yo _____? (salir)

D **Ayer.** Rewrite each sentence using *ayer.* Make all necessary changes.

1. Yo veo una película de horror.

   _____

2. Los actores dan una representación de *El Sombrero de Tres Picos.*

   _____

3. ¿A qué hora salen Uds.?

   _____

4. ¿Aplaudes después del concierto?

   _____

Los complementos indirectos le, les

E **La carta.** Complete with *le, les, lo, la, los,* or *las.* Be careful in deciding whether you need a direct object or an indirect object.

TERESA: Esta noche _____ tengo que escribir una carta a Carmen.
　　　　　　　　　　1

ALEJANDRO: ¿_____ tienes que escribir? ¿Por qué?
　　　　　　2

TERESA: ¿Pues, yo recibí una carta de ella.

ALEJANDRO: ¿Ah, sí? ¿Cuándo _____ recibiste?
　　　　　　　　　　　　　3

TERESA: _____ recibí la semana pasada.
　　　　4

ALEJANDRO: Pues, sí. Es verdad que _____ tienes que escribir.
　　　　　　　　　　　　　　　　5

¿Qué _____ vas a decir?
　　　　6

TERESA: _____ tengo que decir que no puedo asistir a su fiesta.
　　　7

ALEJANDRO: ¿A su fiesta?

TERESA: Sí, sus padres _____ van a dar una fiesta en honor del
　　　　　　　　　　　　8
día de su santo.

ALEJANDRO: ¿_____ escribiste a sus padres también?
　　　　　9

TERESA: No. ¿Por qué me preguntas?

ALEJANDRO: Pues, si no puedes asistir a la fiesta, _____ debes
　　　　　　　　　　　　　　　　　　　　　　10
presentar tus excusas a sus padres también.

TERESA: Tienes razón. Luego _____ voy a escribir una carta
　　　　　　　　　　　　　　11
a Carmen y _____ voy a escribir otra a sus padres.
　　　　　　　12

F **Los complementos.** Rewrite each sentence substituting a pronoun for the indicated object.

1. Ellos vieron *la película* en el cine.

_____

2. Tomás dio la invitación *a sus amigos.*

_____

3. El profesor habló *al estudiante* en español.

_____

UN POCO MÁS

A **Los favoritos.** The magazine *Eres,* published in Mexico, had a survey recently to determine people's favorite stars, shows, etc. Prizes were offered to those who responded. Read the following questionnaire. Vote for your favorites.

MÚSICA

☆ Mejor disco

☆ Mejor cantante (él)

☆ Mejor cantante (ella)

☆ Mejor grupo pop

☆ Mejor grupo de rock

☆ Mejor grupo tropical

☆ Mejor grupo norteño

☆ Mejor show (él)

☆ Mejor show (ella)

CINE
☆ Mejor película

TELEVISIÓN
☆ Mejor telenovela

☆ Mejor director

☆ Mejor productor(a)

☆ Mejor actor

☆ Mejor actriz

☆ Mejor actor coestelar

☆ Mejor actriz coestelar

☆ Mejor tema musical

☆ Mejor programa semanal

TEATRO

☆ Mejor obra dramática

☆ Mejor obra musical

☆ Mejor director

☆ Mejor actor

☆ Mejor acrtiz

☆ Mejor actor coestelar

☆ Mejor actriz coestelar

RADIO
☆ Mejor programa

☆ Mejor locutor

☆ Mejor comercial

Nombre: _____ **Ocupación:** _____

Dirección: _____ **Edad:** _____

¡Contesta rápidamente!, y envía tu carta a:

EDITORIAL ERES, LOS PREMIOS ERES, Apartado postal 5-733 y-750,
C.P. 06500, México, D.F.

B **Una actividad cultural.** Read the following ad that appeared in *El Nuevo Día,* a newspaper in San Juan, Puerto Rico.

Concierto Sinfónico con Luces Láser

con La Orquesta Sinfónica de Puerto Rico a beneficio de
"Te Escuchamos Juventud"

Centro de Bellas Artes, Sábado 13 de marzo

LOS PLANETAS DE HOLTS

Disfrute de la experiencia única de deleitar sus sentidos asistiendo a este novedosísimo concierto, donde por primera vez en Puerto Rico se realizará el más deslumbrante espectáculo musical acompañado de Luces Láser. Bajo la dirección del Maestro Roselín Pabón.

El sistema de Luces Láser estará a cargo de la compañía Laser Spectacles, Inc.
Taquillas: $25.00 planta alta • $30.00 planta baja

TE ESCUCHAMOS
JUVENTUD

C **Los detalles.** In a word or two, answer the questions according to the ad you just read.

1. ¿Qué se va a presentar? _____

2. ¿Cuándo? _____

3. ¿Dónde? _____

4. ¿Cuánto es la entrada en la planta alta? _____

5. ¿Y en la planta baja? _____

D **Expliquen.** Explain what is different or unusual about the concert.

_____

_____

E **¿Quién es?** The following article appeared in the magazine *Vanidades*. As you read the article, try to guess who the article is about before you finish it.

EN LA IMAGEN
DE LA DERECHA
LE VEMOS DE
BEBE, Y EN LA
INFERIOR,
JUNTO CON SU
FAMILIA EN
EUROPA.

**ADIVINE
QUIEN ES...**
Quizás no note su
parecido en la foto en
la que aparece de
bebé, pero en la que
está con su familia, ya
podemos vislumbrar
sus rasgos
¿Profesión? Tenor.
¿Nacionalidad?
Española. Su apellido
es como un día de la
semana, y su nombre,
es un adjetivo que le
viene muy bien al
apellido. Famoso, y
tiene el mérito de
haber hecho que la
juventud mundial se
interese de nuevo por
la ópera. Es...
¡Plácido Domingo...!

MI AUTOBIOGRAFÍA

Everyone gets involved in different cultural activities. Write about a cultural activity that interests you and mention others that you do not have any interest in. Do you watch a lot of television? What programs do you watch? Write about what types of movies you like. Do you go to the movies often? Who are your favorite movie stars? Do you enjoy the arts? If so, write about those that interest you most.

Mi autobiografía

SELF-TEST 3

A Write the name of each item or person.

1. _____

2. _____

3. _____

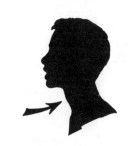

4. _____

5. _____

6. _____

7. _____

8. _____

9. _____

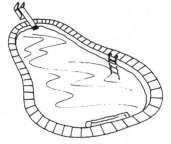

10. _____

11. _____

12. _____

B Match the word in the left column with its opposite in the right column.

1. _____ bajar   **a.** alquilar
2. _____ el invierno   **b.** el verano
3. _____ frío   **c.** enfermo
4. _____ el patinaje sobre hielo   **d.** subir
5. _____ contento   **e.** calor
6. _____ bien   **f.** ayer
7. _____ comprar   **g.** el patinaje sobre ruedas
8. _____ hay sol   **h.** volver
9. _____ hoy   **i.** triste
10. _____ salir   **j.** está nublado

C Choose an appropriate expression in the right column to match each verb in the left column.

1. bajar _____   tenis
2. subir _____   enfermo
3. estar _____   una propina
4. tener _____   la pista
5. abrir _____   la gripe
6. tomar _____   en el telesquí
7. jugar _____   una película
8. pagar _____   la boca
9. dejar _____   la cuenta
10. ver _____   medicamento, medicina

D Complete each sentence with the appropriate word(s).

1. Ellos _____ en el verano y esquían en el _____.
2. Los _____ suben la montaña en el _____.
3. Él estornuda mucho porque tiene _____.
4. Cuando uno tiene fiebre, frecuentemente tiene dolor de _____ también.
5. El paciente _____ la boca cuando el médico le examina la

   _____.

6. El médico _____ los medicamentos y el _____ los despacha.
7. Cuando hay nubes, no hay _____. Está _____.
8. El _____ es un tipo de tren subterráneo que corre debajo de la tierra.

E Complete each sentence with the correct form of *saber* or *conocer.*

1. Yo _____ a Roberto.

2. Yo _____ donde vive.

3. Él _____ mi número de teléfono.

4. Yo _____ que Roberto _____ muy bien la literatura española.

F Complete each sentence with the correct form of *ser* or *estar.*

1. Madrid _____ en España.

2. Madrid _____ la capital de España.

3. La ciudad _____ grande.

4. Mi amiga Sandra _____ de Madrid.

5. Ella siempre _____ contenta.

6. Ella _____ alta y rubia.

7. Su casa _____ en el barrio Salamanca.

G Complete each sentence with the correct form of *decir.*

1. Yo _____ la verdad.

2. Él _____ que va a salir.

3. Nosotros _____ la misma cosa.

4. ¿Y qué _____ Uds.?

H Complete each sentence with the correct pronoun: *me, te, nos, le, les, lo, la, los, las.*

1. ¿_____ examina el médico?

    Sí, me examina en su consultorio.

2. ¿Les hablan a Uds. sus amigos?

    Sí, ellos _____ hablan.

3. ¿Le hablaste a Juan?

    Sí, _____ hablé.

4. ¿Viste a María?

    Sí, _____ vi.

5. ¿Lee Juan el periódico?

    Sí, _____ lee.

6. ¿Miras las fotografías?

    Sí, _____ miro.

I Rewrite each sentence in the preterite.

1. Yo nado en el mar.

   _____

2. Mis amigos bucean.

   _____

3. ¿Alquilas un barco?

   _____

4. ¿Toman Uds. el sol?

   _____

5. ¿Usas una crema protectora?

   _____

6. Ellos suben la montaña en el telesquí.

   _____

7. Yo pierdo mis gafas.

   _____

8. ¿Comes mucho?

   _____

9. ¿Quién te da las lecciones?

   _____

10. Veo la película.

    _____

11. Juego (al) fútbol.

    _____

12. Ya empiezo.

    _____

J Choose the correct response.

1. ¿Cómo suben la montaña?
   a. en la taquilla
   b. en el metro
   c. en el telesilla

2. ¿Dónde hay estaciones de esquí?
   a. en Puerto Rico
   b. en todos los países hispanos
   c. en España, Chile y la Argentina

3. ¿Qué montañas están al norte de Madrid?
   a. la sierra de Guadarrama
   b. la sierra Nevada
   c. los Andes

4. ¿Qué están presentando en el Cine Liceo?
   a. una película de horror
   b. la obra de un dramaturgo contemporáneo
   c. una exposición de arte moderno

5. ¿Qué pinta el artista?
   a. una estatua en bronce
   b. un cuadro
   c. una exposición

K Tell whether each statement is true or false.

1. _____ La manía por los ejercicios físicos existe más en los países hispanos que en los Estados Unidos.
2. _____ El SIDA es un problema médico serio.
3. _____ Cuando es el invierno en el hemisferio norte es el verano en el hemisferio sur.
4. _____ Hay muchas playas fantásticas en muchas partes del mundo hispano.

Answers appear on pages 179–180.

CAPÍTULO

13

LA ROPA Y LA MODA

VOCABULARIO

Palabras 1

A **La tienda de ropa para caballeros.** Write the name of each item in the illustration.

1. _____   5. _____
2. _____   6. _____
3. _____   7. _____
4. _____   8. _____

B **De compras.** Complete each sentence with the appropriate word(s).

1. Roberto no paga con un cheque. Paga con una _____.

2. Él paga en la _____.

3. En la tienda él compra un par de _____.

4. Los tenis no cuestan mucho. No son muy _____. Son bastante

   _____.

5. Los tenis le _____ bien. No son ni grandes ni pequeños.

Palabras 2

C ¿Qué es? Write the name of each item.

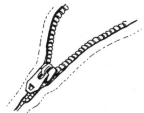 

1. _____ 2. _____ 3. _____

D Lo contrario. Write the opposite of each of the following.

1. corto _____   5. me aprieta _____

2. grande _____   6. el dependiente _____

3. ancho _____   7. blanco _____

4. caro _____   8. alto _____

E Lo mismo. Rewrite each sentence using another expression that means the same as the indicated expression.

1. Esta camisa *me queda* bien.

_____

2. Este pantalón tiene *zíper.*

_____

3. Es *una chaqueta* a cuadros.

_____

4. ¿Cuál es su *talla?*

_____

F Para señoras y señores. List five articles of clothing worn by both men and women.

1. _____
2. _____
3. _____
4. _____
5. _____

G   **Para señores.** Describe the outfits Eugenio and Paco are wearing in the following illustration.

_____

_____

_____

_____

H   **Para señoras.** Describe the outfits Virginia and Adela are wearing in the following illustration.

_____

_____

_____

_____

ESTRUCTURA

Verbos como interesar y aburrir

A **¿A quién le interesa?** Write sentences according to the model.

Juan dice que la historia es interesante.
A Juan le interesa la historia.

1. Yo digo que la historia es interesante.

   _____

2. Nosotros decimos que la historia es interesante.

   _____

3. Roberto dice que la historia es interesante.

   _____

4. Teresa dice que la historia es interesante.

   _____

5. ¿Dices que la historia es interesante?

   _____

6. Ellos dicen que la historia es interesante.

   _____

B **¿A quién le aburre?** Write sentences according to the model.

Yo encuentro las novelas policíacas muy aburridas.
Las novelas policíacas me aburren.

1. Juan encuentra las telenovelas muy aburridas.

   _____

2. Encontramos las ciencias muy aburridas.

   _____

3. Ellos encuentran estas conversaciones muy aburridas.

   _____

4. ¿Encuentras sus conversaciones aburridas?

   _____

El verbo gustar

C **La verdad es que nos encanta.** Rewrite each sentence changing *gustar* to *encantar*.

1. Me gusta esta camisa.

   _____

2. A Juan le gustan los tenis.

   _____

3. ¿Te gusta el color azul marino?

   _____

4. Nos gusta el estilo "sport".

   _____

5. A ellos les gustan los blue jeans.

   _____

D **Lo quiero porque me gusta.** Answer each question according to the model.

   ¿Quieres esta camisa?
   Sí, la quiero. Me gusta.

1. ¿Quieres estas medias?

   _____

2. ¿Quieres estos tenis?

   _____

3. ¿María quiere esta blusa?

   _____

4. ¿Carlos quiere estos zapatos?

   _____

5. ¿Quieren Uds. este saco?

   _____

6. ¿Quieren Uds. estos pantalones?

   _____

E **Lo que me gusta hacer.** Write five things you like to do.

1. _____

2. _____

3. _____

4. _____

5. _____

F **¿Por qué no?** Write five things you do not like and tell why.

1. _____

2. _____

3. _____

4. _____

5. _____

G **¿Por qué?** Write five things you like and tell why.

1. _____

2. _____

3. _____

4. _____

5. _____

Las palabras negativas y afirmativas

H **Lo contrario.** Match the word in the left column with its opposite in the right column.

1. _____ siempre   **a.** nadie

2. _____ algo   **b.** no

3. _____ alguien   **c.** nunca

4. _____ sí   **d.** nada

5. _____ también   **e.** tampoco

6. _____ ni yo tampoco   **f.** y yo también

I **En la forma negativa.** Rewrite each sentence in the negative.

1. Él tiene algo en la mano.

_____

2. Alguien lo conoce.

_____

3. Yo siempre voy allí.

_____

4. ¿Tiene él pesos o sucres?

_____

5. Yo siempre leo algo.

_____

6. Anita quiere algo también.

_____

7. Nosotros vemos a alguien.

_____

J **¿Por qué?** Write six original sentences in the negative.

1. _____

2. _____

3. _____

4. _____

5. _____

6. _____

UN POCO MÁS

A **Una entrevista.** En España y en Latinoamérica hay muchas revistas para los jóvenes como Uds. En las revistas hay artículos sobre la moda, los deportes, los intereses y los gustos de los jóvenes. A veces en estas revistas hay una entrevista con una persona famosa. Aquí tenemos una entrevista que apareció recientemente en una revista mexicana.

Nombre completo	Ángel Ibarra de Solís
Edad	18 años
Estatura	1.85 metros
Peso	como 66 kilos
Talla	30 con cinturón. El 29 me queda apretado.
Fecha de nacimiento	8 de septiembre
Signo de zodíaco	Virgo: Me gusta ser Virgo porque tengo muchos amigos y amigas que son Virgo.
Lugar de nacimiento	México, D.F.
Carácter	Soy calmado por lo general, me gusta comprender a la gente pero también me enoja la gente cuando hacen cosas que no comprendo.
Comida preferida	Me gustan las pizzas y el pollo.
Ropa preferida	Un blue jean de denim, una camisa amplia y un blazer
Mayor defecto	A veces hablo cuando no debo.
Mayor cualidad	Soy muy organizado.
La cocina	Me gusta y la hago muy bien.
Músicos que admira	Mozart, Sting y Petruco, un guitarrista mexicano excelente
Lo que más me molesta	Me molestan la ignorancia y la hipocresía.
Pasatiempos	Ver películas, salir los fines de semana y sobre todo ir a San Miguel de Allende a tocar con una banda
Deporte favorito	Mi prioridad es ser músico, después, detective y después futbolista.
Lo que más me gusta	La expresión de los ojos

B **Preguntas.** Answer the questions based on the preceding magazine article.

1. ¿Cuál es la talla del cinturón de Ángel?

_____

2. ¿Cómo le queda el 29?

_____

3. ¿Por qué le gusta ser Virgo?

_____

4. ¿Cuándo le enoja la gente?

   _____

5. A Ángel, ¿qué comidas le gustan?

   _____

6. ¿Le gusta la cocina?

   _____

7. ¿Cuáles son algunas cosas que le molestan?

   _____

C **Una entrevista personal.** Change *Nombre completo* in the preceding article to your own name and then complete with personal information.

Nombre completo _____

Edad _____

Estatura _____

Peso _____

Talla _____

Fecha de nacimiento _____

Signo de zodíaco _____

Lugar de nacimiento _____

Carácter _____

Comida preferida _____

Ropa preferida _____

Mayor defecto _____

Mayor cualidad _____

La cocina _____

Músicos que admiro _____

Lo que más me molesta _____

Pasatiempos _____

Deporte favorito _____

Lo que más me gusta _____

MI AUTOBIOGRAFÍA

Some people love to shop for clothes and others do not. Write about yourself. If you like to shop for clothes, tell about your shopping habits. What kind of stores do you go to, etc.? If you do not like shopping, tell why not. Tell what kinds of clothes you like and those that you do not like. You may want to include your present sizes for certain articles of clothing. Describe your favorite outfit.

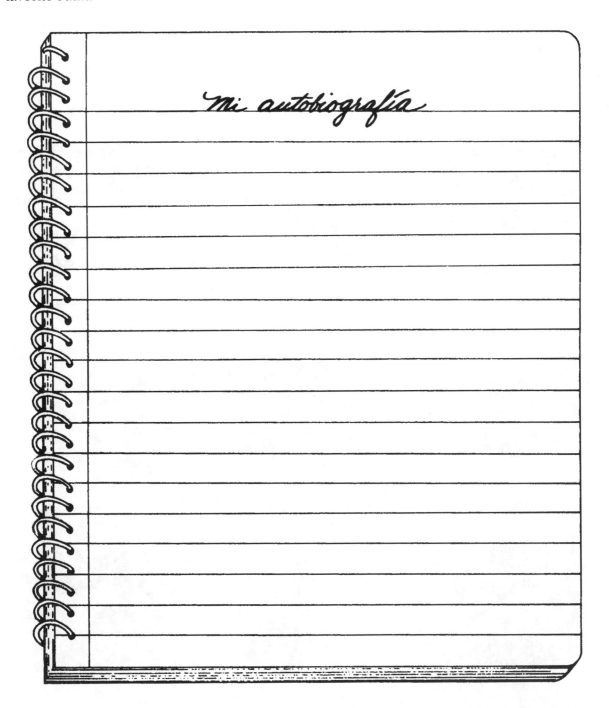

mi autobiografía

CAPÍTULO

14

UN VIAJE EN TREN

VOCABULARIO

Palabras 1

A ¿Qué es o quién es? Write the name of each item or person.

1. _____

2. _____

3. _____

4. _____

5. _____

6. _____

7. _____

8. _____

9. _____

B **En el andén.** Write five sentences about the illustration.

1. _____

2. _____

3. _____

4. _____

5. _____

Palabras 2

C **Lo contrario.** Match the word or expression in the left column with its opposite in the right column.

1. _____ subir al tren   **a.** tarde

2. _____ libre   **b.** bajar del tren

3. _____ a tiempo   **c.** el billete sencillo

4. _____ el billete de ida y vuelta   **d.** la llegada

5. _____ la salida   **e.** ocupado

D **El sinónimo.** Match the word or expression in the left column with a word or expression that means the same in the right column.

1. _____ el mozo   **a.** la boletería

2. _____ la ventanilla   **b.** cambiar de tren

3. _____ el vagón   **c.** con una demora

4. _____ el billete   **d.** el maletero

5. _____ transbordar   **e.** el boleto

6. _____ con retraso   **f.** el coche

E **Frases originales.** Write an original sentence according to each illustration.

1. _____

_____

2. _____

_____

3. _____

_____

4. _____

_____

5. _____

_____

6. _____

_____

ESTRUCTURA

El pretérito de los verbos hacer, querer y venir

A **En el pasado.** Rewrite each sentence in the preterite.

1. No lo quiero hacer.

    _____

2. No lo hago.

    _____

3. No vengo.

    _____

4. ¿Por qué no lo quieres hacer?

    _____

5. ¿Uds. no lo hacen?

    _____

6. ¿Por qué no vienen?

    _____

7. Nosotros lo hacemos a tiempo.

    _____

El pretérito de otros verbos irregulares

B **Un accidente, pero no serio.** Complete each sentence with the correct preterite form(s) of the indicated verb(s).

1. Unos cien pasajeros _____ a bordo del tren cuando _____ lugar (ocurrió) el accidente. (estar, tener)
2. Nosotros no _____ nada del accidente. (saber)
3. Como Uds. no _____ nada, no _____ hacer nada, ¿verdad? (saber, poder)
4. Exactamente. Pero cuando ellos no llegaron a mi casa, yo _____ una llamada telefónica. (hacer)
5. Pero yo _____ que esperar mucho tiempo para saber algo porque nadie contestó el (al) teléfono. (tener)

C **Un viaje por España.** Complete each sentence with the correct preterite form(s) of the indicated verb(s).

1. Ellos _____ un viaje a España. (hacer)

2. Ellos _____ por todo el país. (andar)

3. Desgraciadamente no _____ ir a Galicia en el noroeste porque no _____ bastante tiempo. (poder, tener)

4. Ellos _____ casi un mes entero en Andalucía, en el sur. (estar)

D **El tren.** Rewrite each sentence in the preterite.

1. Yo hago un viaje con mi hermana.

   _____

2. Hacemos el viaje en tren.

   _____

3. No queremos hacer el viaje en coche.

   _____

4. El tren está completo.

   _____

5. Nosotros no podemos encontrar un asiento libre.

   _____

6. Nosotros estamos de pie en el pasillo.

   _____

7. Nosotros tenemos que transbordar en Segovia.

   _____

8. Podemos encontrar un asiento libre en el otro tren.

   _____

9. Estamos muy cómodos en este tren.

   _____

UN POCO MÁS

A **El tren en Costa Rica.** Read the following about a train line in Costa Rica.

El tren que va de San José a Puerto Limón en Costa Rica se debe a Henry Meiggs, un norteamericano legendario. Meiggs fue responsable de la construcción del Ferrocarril Central en los Andes del Perú. El gobierno de Costa Rica invitó a Meiggs a construir un ferrocarril de Puerto Limón a la capital. Meiggs hizo responsable de la obra a su sobrino, Minor C. Keith. Terminaron la construcción en 1891. Keith construyó el ferrocarril y también desarrolló la industria bananera en Costa Rica. Él fue uno de los fundadores de la United Fruit Company en 1899.

B **Los detalles.** Answer each question according to the reading.

1. ¿Qué ciudades enlaza el tren?

_____

2. ¿Quién fue Henry Meiggs?

_____

3. ¿Quién fue Minor C. Keith?

_____

4. ¿Quién construyó el ferrocarril de Costa Rica?

_____

5. ¿Qué desarrolló (developed) Keith?

_____

6. ¿Qué compañía fundó?

_____

7. ¿Cuándo la fundó?

_____

C **Los moros.** In Toledo many tourists visit the *Alcázar*, an Arab palace. Toledo is just one of many areas in Spain where one can find a great deal of Moorish or Arab influence. Read the following to find out why these influences are present.

> Si miramos un mapa podemos ver que España
> está muy cerca del norte de África. En los países
> del norte de África viven los moros o los árabes.
> En el año 711 los árabes invadieron a España.
> Ocuparon casi todo el país y no salieron hasta
> 1492. Después de ocho siglos de ocupación
> árabe, hay mucha influencia mora o musulmana
> en España.

D **Preguntas.** Answer each question according to the reading in Exercise C.

1. ¿España está cerca de qué continente?

   _____

2. ¿Quiénes vivieron en los países del norte de África?

   _____

3. ¿En qué año invadieron los árabes a España?

   _____

4. ¿En qué año salieron los árabes de España?

   _____

5. ¿Cuántos siglos estuvieron los árabes en España?

   _____

E **Palabras afines.** Find eight cognates used in the reading in Exercise C about the Moorish influence in Spain.

1. _____   5. _____
2. _____   6. _____
3. _____   7. _____
4. _____   8. _____

F **Adivinen.** There are two other words used in the reading that you might not know. They are not cognates, but you can guess what they mean from the way they are used in the sentence. Choose the correct word(s) to complete each statement.

1. *Cerca de* means _____.
    a. near
    b. far away
    c. circle

2. *Siglo* means _____.
    a. year
    b. month
    c. century

G **Palabras árabes.** Read the following information.

Note that the word *alcázar* begins with *al-*. One of the interesting things about languages is that they will very often borrow words from another language. After eight centuries of Moorish occupation, quite a few Arabic words found their way into the Spanish language. Most of the Arabic words used in Spanish begin with *al-*. Here are some other examples:

Spanish	Arabic
la almohada	*al muhadda*
el alcalde	*al qadi*

H **Influencia griega.** Read the following information.

Before the invasion of the Moors, the Greeks also occupied a part of Spain. There are also some words of Greek origin that are used in Spanish. Most of the words of Greek origin resemble English words as well. However, these words do not follow the usual pattern in Spanish. They end in -a, but are masculine nouns and take masculine articles and adjectives. This is because the -a ending in Greek is a masculine, not a feminine ending.

I **Palabras griegas.** Here are some words of Greek origin. Would you have any difficulty guessing the meaning of each?

el mapa   el sistema
el drama   el poema
el programa   el clima

MI AUTOBIOGRAFÍA

Do you ever travel by train? If so, tell about one of your train trips. If you have never taken a train trip, make one up. Imagine you are traveling by train in Spain and write something about your trip. Tell whether or not you think train travel is interesting. If you never travel by train, explain why you don't.

mi autobiografía

CAPÍTULO 15

EN EL RESTAURANTE

VOCABULARIO

Palabras 1

A **Voy a poner la mesa.** Write a list of the things you need to set the dinner table.

_____

_____

_____

_____

B **¿Quién es?** Write the name of the person being described.

1. el que prepara la comida, el que cocina _____
2. el que sirve a los clientes en el restaurante _____
3. el que come en el restaurante _____
4. el que pide el menú _____
5. el que trae el menú _____
6. el que deja la propina _____
7. el que recibe la propina _____
8. el que le trae la cuenta _____
9. el que pide y paga la cuenta _____

C **¿Sí o no?** Tell whether each statement is true or false.

1. _____ Muchas veces puedes pagar la cuenta con una tarjeta de crédito.
2. _____ Bebes mucho si tienes hambre.
3. _____ El mesero prepara las papas.
4. _____ El menú es una lista de los platos que sirven en el restaurante.
5. _____ Si usas demasiada sal, vas a tener mucha sed.
6. _____ El mesero sirve la comida en una taza.

Palabras 2

D ¿Qué es? Write the name of each item.

1. _____   2. _____   3. _____

4. _____   5. _____   6. _____

7. _____   8. _____   9. _____

E **Lo que yo quisiera comer.** Prepare a menu that would please you.

_____

_____

_____

_____

_____

ESTRUCTURA

El presente de los verbos con el cambio e > i

A **Yo no, todos nosotros.** Rewrite each sentence in the plural (*nosotros*).

1. Yo pido una ensalada.

   _____

2. Yo sirvo muchas verduras.

   _____

3. Yo sigo un régimen.

   _____

4. Yo no frío casi nada.

   _____

B **En el restaurante.** Complete each sentence with the correct present tense form(s) of the indicated verb(s).

1. El mesero les _____ a los clientes lo que ellos le _____.
   (servir, pedir)

2. Si el cliente _____ papas fritas, el cocinero las _____.
   (pedir, freír)

3. A veces si hay un plato que me gusta mucho, yo lo _____ otra vez. (pedir)

4. Si el mesero me _____ bien, yo le dejo una propina. (servir)

C **¿Qué le gusta?** Answer the questions according to the model.

   ¿Le gusta a Juanita el pollo?
   Sí, y siempre lo pide.

1. ¿Te gustan los huevos fritos?

   _____

2. ¿Les gusta a Uds. la ensalada con aceite y vinagre?

   _____

3. ¿Les gusta a Carlos y a Felipe el biftec a término medio?

   _____

El pretérito de los verbos con el cambio e > i, o > u

D **En el pasado.** Rewrite each sentence in the preterite.

1. Yo como lo que pido.

   _____

2. Él me sirve lo que pido.

   _____

3. Él me repite lo que le pido.

   _____

4. El cocinero me sugiere el biftec a término medio.

   _____

5. Pero el mesero me sirve la carne casi cruda.

   _____

6. Yo no como el biftec que él me sirve.

   _____

E **Preguntas personales.** Give your own answers.

1. ¿Cuántas horas duermes cada noche?

   _____

2. ¿Cuántas horas dormiste anoche?

   _____

3. ¿Quiénes duermen en un hotel?

   _____

4. ¿En qué hotel durmieron los turistas anoche?

   _____

UN POCO MÁS

A **Un anuncio.** Read the following advertisement.

¿DÓNDE COMEMOS?

EL PLAT. Conde de Altea, 41. Valencia.
Tel. 334 96 38. Cierre, lunes y festivos noche.

Comer un arroz dignamente hecho es uno de los mayores deseos de cualquier visitante de la capital valenciana, deseo que demasiado a menudo queda frustrado, porque no son muchos los locales que incluyen arroces en sus cartas o porque no los hacen muy bien.

"El Plat" constituye una excepción. Se hace en esta casa, limpia, pequeña y agradable, un plato del día, cada jornada distinto, con arroz. Es excelente el de bacalao que sirven los domingos, pero cada día vale la pena.

B **"El Plat".** Choose the correct word or expression to complete each sentence, according to the ad.

1. La persona que escribió este artículo es un crítico de _____.
   a. arte
   b. cocina
   c. teatro

2. "El Plat" es _____.
   a. una persona
   b. una calle
   c. un restaurante

3. La especialidad de "El Plat" es _____.
   a. el vino
   b. el arroz
   c. el menudo

4. El cocinero siempre prepara el plato del día con _____.
   a. bacalao
   b. arroz
   c. vino

5. No es posible ir a "El Plat" los _____.
   a. lunes
   b. sábados
   c. domingos

6. Conde de Altea es _____.
   a. la calle donde está "El Plat"
   b. el propietario de "El Plat"
   c. el autor del artículo

C **¿Cómo se dice?** How do you say the following in Spanish?

1. special of the day _____
2. is worthwhile _____
3. different each day _____

D ¡**A comer!** Read the following ad that appeared in a magazine in Puerto Rico. Then choose the correct responses according to the ad.

1. ¿Qué es esto?

   a. un anuncio

   b. una crítica

   c. una receta

2. ¿Cuándo cierra?

   a. los miércoles y jueves

   b. los sábados y domingos

   c. los lunes y martes

3. ¿Quién paga un precio reducido?

   a. Zaida Clemons

   b. los niños

   c. las personas con reservaciones

4. ¿Qué no está incluído en el precio de $10.95?

   a. los platos "créole"

   b. la sopa de queso

   c. el postre

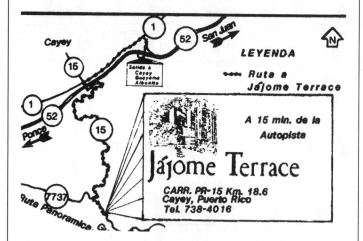

**RESERVACIONES SON INDISPENSABLES
DESPUES DE LAS 6:00 P.M.
738-4016**
Aceptamos las principales tarjetas de crédito.

Jájome Terrace

A 15 min. de la Autopista

Jájome Terrace
CARR. PR-15 Km. 18.6
Cayey, Puerto Rico
Tel. 738-4016

¡TODO LO QUE PUEDA COMER!

por SOLO **$10.95**

Bebidas y Postre Adicional
(niños menores de 12 años-a mitad de precio)
**DISFRUTE NUESTRAS
DELICIOSAS ENSALADAS, FAMOSA SOPA DE QUESO,
PLATOS "CREOLE", CLIMA (65°F-75°F)
Y VISTA PANORAMICA DEL MAR CARIBE**
ABIERTO
Miércoles a Sábado
12:00 del mediodía hasta 9:00 p.m.
Domingos y Días Feriados
12:00 del mediodía hasta 6:00 p.m.
Atendido por su dueña
Zaida Clemons

E **Adivinen.** Figure it out or guess, according to the ad.

1. Besides the food, what else does the ad stress as an attraction?
   _____ vista Panoramica Pa mar caribe _____

2. Can you eat there after 6 P.M. or not? Explain.
   _____ Si, nuevo es hasta _____

3. Where is Jájome Terrace?
   _____ cayey, PR _____

4. Can you pay with a credit card? If so, with which card(s)?
   _____ Si, ~~Bebidas Postre~~ _____

5. Who is the owner?
   _____ ~~...~~ _____

6. What is a specialty of the restaurant?
   _____ ensalatas _____

7. How much can one eat for $10.95?
   _____ Disfute, ensalada, creole _____

8. When is the restaurant usually closed?
   _____ Seis _____

F **Las abreviaturas.** Look at the ad again. Find the abbreviation for each of the following words.

1. teléfono _____ fono _____
2. minutos _____ min _____
3. Puerto Rico _____ PR _____
4. kilómetro _____ Km _____
5. carretera _____ carr _____

MI AUTOBIOGRAFÍA

Tell whether or not you like to eat in a restaurant. If you do, tell which restaurant(s) you go to. Give a description of a dinner out. You know quite a few words for foods in Spanish. Write about which foods you like and those you do not like.

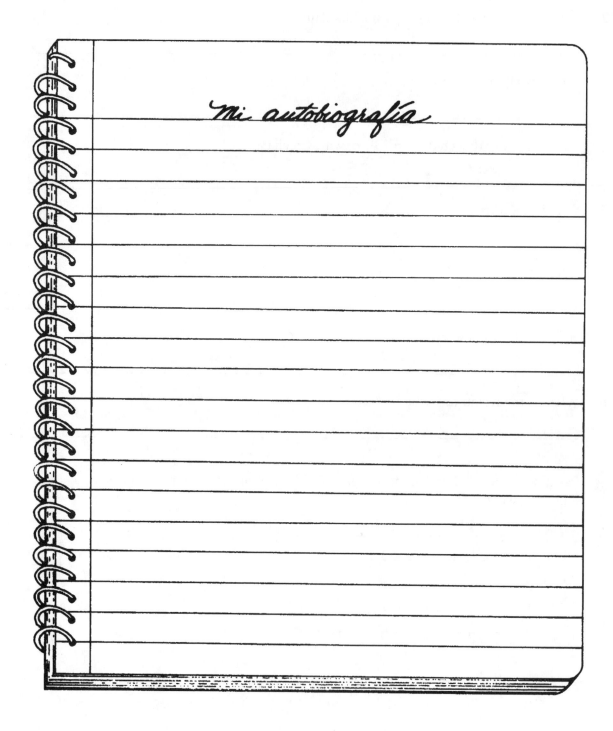

mi autobiografía

CAPÍTULO 16

EL CAMPING

VOCABULARIO

Palabras 1

A **¿Qué es?** Write the name of each item.

1. _____ 2. _____ 3. _____

4. _____ 5. _____

B **El cuerpo humano.** Identify as many parts of the body as you can.

_____

_____

_____

_____

C **A escoger.** Choose the correct verb to complete each sentence.

1. Él _____ José.
   a. se lava
   b. se llama
   c. se levanta

2. La muchacha _____ a las once de la noche.
   a. se acuesta
   b. se levanta
   c. se despierta

3. El joven _____ el pelo cada día.
   a. se lava
   b. se viste
   c. se pone

4. Ella _____ la ropa.
   a. se lava
   b. se pone
   c. se mira

5. El muchacho _____ y luego se levanta.
   a. se duerme
   b. se lava
   c. se despierta

6. Él se mira en el espejo mientras _____.
   a. se pone
   b. se desayuna
   c. se afeita

Palabras 2

D **¿Qué es?** Write the name of each item.

1. _____   2. _____   3. _____

4. _____   5. _____   6. _____

E   **En la farmacia.** Complete with the appropriate word.

1. Un _____ de pasta dentífrica, por favor.
2. Un _____ de papel higiénico.
3. Una _____ de jabón.

F   **Un pequeño diccionario.** Write the word being defined.

1. pasar una o varias noches en un camping o campamento _____
2. un tipo de cama que se usa durante las vacaciones de camping _____
3. un tipo de casa o casita de lona (*canvas*) o de plástico que se arma o se levanta
    en un camping _____
4. lo que se usa para lavarse el pelo _____
5. lo que se usa para lavarse _____
6. lo que se usa para lavarse o cepillarse los dientes _____
7. lo que se usa para afeitarse _____
8. lo que se usa para preparar la comida _____

G   **¿Qué es?** Write the name of each item.

1. _____

2. _____

3. _____

4. _____

5. _____

6. _____

ESTRUCTURA

Los verbos reflexivos

A **Preguntas personales.** Give your own answers.

1. ¿Cómo te llamas?

   _____

2. ¿A qué hora te levantas?

   _____

3. ¿Dónde (te) desayunas?

   _____

4. ¿Te cepillas los dientes después del desayuno?

   _____

5. Por la mañana, ¿te bañas o tomas una ducha?

   _____

6. ¿Te miras en el espejo cuando te peinas?

   _____

B **Un día típico.** Complete each sentence with the correct reflexive pronoun(s).

1. Yo _____ despierto y _____ levanto en seguida.
2. Mi hermano y yo _____ levantamos a la misma hora.
3. Yo _____ lavo y luego él _____ lava.
4. Nosotros no _____ lavamos al mismo tiempo en el cuarto de baño.
5. Mis amigos _____ cepillan los dientes después de cada comida.
6. Y ellos _____ lavan las manos antes de comer.

C **Yo.** Complete with the appropriate words.

Yo _____ lavo _____ manos y _____
       1   2   3

cara. _____ cepillo _____ dientes y _____
       4   5   6

cepillo _____ pelo. Yo _____ pongo _____
       7   8   9

ropa.

Los verbos reflexivos de cambio radical

D **La rutina.** Complete each sentence with the correct present tense form(s) of the verb(s).

1. Yo _____ y me levanto en seguida. (despertarse)

2. Mi hermana y yo bajamos a la cocina y _____ a la mesa. (sentarse)

3. Después de tomar el desayuno, yo _____ y ella _____.
   (vestirse, vestirse)

4. Después de las clases, yo _____ con mis amigos. Nosotros
   _____ mucho. (divertirse, divertirse)

5. Cuando yo _____, _____ en seguida. (acostarse, dormirse)

6. Y tú, ¿ _____ en seguida cuando _____?
   (dormirse, acostarse)

E **En el pasado.** Rewrite each sentence in the preterite.

1. Ellos se sientan a la mesa.

   _____

2. Él se acuesta y se duerme en seguida.

   _____

3. Desgraciadamente yo no me duermo en seguida.

   _____

4. Él se viste elegantemente.

   _____

5. Los amigos se divierten mucho.

   _____

6. ¿A qué hora te acuestas?

   _____

7. Yo me visto en seguida.

   _____

8. Nosotros nos sentamos a la mesa para tomar el desayuno.

   _____

F **Frases originales.** Make up an original sentence using each of the following verbs.

1. llamarse

   _____

2. llamar

   _____

3. lavarse

   _____

4. lavar

   _____

5. mirarse

   _____

6. mirar

   _____

7. divertirse

   _____

8. divertir

   _____

9. ponerse

   _____

10. poner

    _____

11. peinarse

    _____

12. peinar

    _____

UN POCO MÁS

A **Convivir con la naturaleza.** Read the following that appeared in *El ABC,* a Madrid newspaper. To understand it, you need to know the following words: *hoguera* (bonfire), *arder* (to burn), *fuego* (fire).

EXCURSIONISTA

Tu hoguera puede hacer arder el monte.
Respeta la prohibición de encender fuego en verano y las normas para convivir con la naturaleza.

Recuerda que los cristales, la basura y las colillas encendidas son elementos que propician los incendios forestales.

No conviertas el monte en una hoguera.

B **A escoger.** Choose the correct word or expression to complete each sentence.

1. This ad is directed to _____.
   a. campers
   b. firefighters
   c. swimmers

2. Campfires are not allowed _____.
   a. in the woods
   b. during the summer
   c. at night

C **El sinónimo.** Match the Spanish word or expression in the left column with its English equivalent in the right column.

1. _____ hoguera
2. _____ cristales
3. _____ colillas encendidas
4. _____ incendios forestales
5. _____ la naturaleza
6. _____ la basura

a. lit cigarette butts
b. forest fires
c. nature
d. glass
e. campfire
f. garbage

D **Los cristales.** Explain the problem with *los cristales.*

_____

_____

E **Para acampar.** Look at the following ad that appeared in *El Nuevo Día*, a San Juan newspaper.

Para acampar con estilo...

Caseta 10' X 8'
Wenzel, estilo Evergreen
Reg. 152.95
ESP. **129.88**

Caseta 12' x 9'
Wenzel, estilo Evergreen
No ilustrada.
Reg. 189.95
ESP. **149.88**

Dining Canopy
Wenzel. Estilo Everegreen.
11½" x 11½"
Reg. 36.95
ESP. **29.88**

Ofertas válidas del 16 al 28 de julio

González Padín
SIEMPRE ES CALIDAD

Aceptamos UniCuenta, Master Card, Visa, Ideal, Diner's y American Express

F **A escoger.** Choose the correct word or expression to complete each sentence.

1. El precio especial de la caseta más grande es _____.
   a. 2129.88
   b. 149.88
   c. 189.55

2. El nombre de la tienda por departamentos es _____.
   a. González Padín
   b. Wenzel
   c. Evergreen

3. La oferta es válida por _____.
   a. una semana
   b. dos semanas
   c. un mes

4. La tienda acepta seis diferentes _____.
   a. casetas
   b. estilos
   c. tarjetas

MI AUTOBIOGRAFÍA

Every day there are certain routine things we all have to do. Give as much information as you can about your daily routine. Include what time you usually do each thing. Then tell whether or not you go camping. If you do, tell where you like to go. What do you do when you first get to camp? Tell if your routine changes when you go camping. If you do not like to camp or never go, tell why.

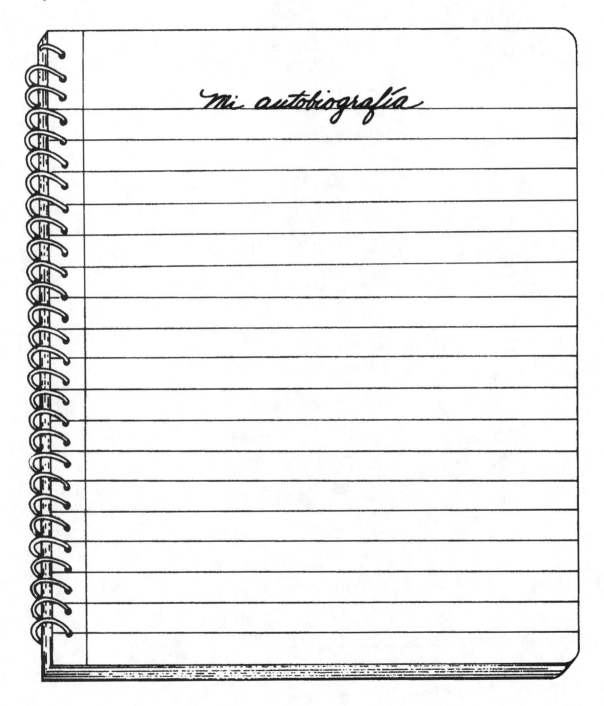

Mi autobiografía

SELF-TEST 4

A Write the name of each item.

1. _____   2. _____   3. _____

4. _____   5. _____   6. _____

7. _____   8. _____   9. _____

B Complete each sentence with the appropriate word.

1. Los _____ esperan el tren en la sala de espera.

2. Compran su boleto en la _____.

3. Si quieren volver a la misma ciudad, compran un boleto (billete) de _____.

4. Venden periódicos y revistas en el _____.

5. El _____ ayuda a los pasajeros con su equipaje.

Nombre _____ Fecha _____

C Write the name of each item.

1. _____ 2. _____ 3. _____

4. _____ 5. _____ 6. _____

D Complete each sentence with the appropriate word.

1. El muchacho va a tomar una ducha. Necesita una _____ de jabón.

2. La muchacha quiere peinarse. Necesita un _____.

3. Ella _____ por la mañana y se acuesta por la noche.

4. El muchacho _____ los dientes.

E Write the opposite of each of the following words.

1. ancho _____

2. alto _____

3. corto _____

4. negro _____

5. la llegada _____

6. libre _____

7. bajar del tren _____

8. a tiempo _____

9. las legumbres _____

10. casi crudo _____

11. sentarse _____

12. dormirse _____

13. temprano _____

14. caro _____

F Complete each sentence according to the model.

Juan va a comprar estas camisas…
Juan va a comprar estas camisas porque le gustan.

1. Voy a comprar esta camisa…

   _____

2. Ellos van a comprar la raqueta…

   _____

3. Vas a comprar el blue jean…

   _____

4. Ellos van a comprar los tenis…

   _____

5. Yo voy a comprar los zapatos…

   _____

6. Vamos a comprar el disco…

   _____

G Rewrite each sentence in the negative.

1. Tiene algo.

   _____

2. Ella ve a alguien en la sala.

   _____

3. Ellos siempre viajan.

   _____

4. Yo viajo también.

   _____

5. ¿Tienes lápiz o bolígrafo?

   _____

H Complete each sentence with the correct preterite form of the indicated verb.

1. Él no _____ hacer el viaje. (querer)
2. Sus amigos _____ el viaje. (hacer)
3. Yo no _____ ir. (poder)
4. Mis amigos _____ a mi casa. (venir)
5. ¿_____ tú las maletas en la maletera? (poner)
6. Nosotros _____ por toda España. (andar)
7. Ellos _____ allí. (estar)
8. Yo _____ más tarde. (venir)

I Complete each sentence with the correct present tense form of the indicated verb.

1. En el restaurante yo _____ un biftec. (pedir)
2. Mi hermano lo _____ bien hecho. (pedir)
3. El mesero nos _____. (servir)
4. Nosotros _____ el plato otra vez. (pedir)
5. Nosotros le _____ la cuenta. (pedir)

J Rewrite each sentence from Exercise I in the preterite.

1. _____
2. _____
3. _____
4. _____
5. _____

K Complete each sentence with a pronoun when necessary.

1. Yo _____ lavo mi carro.
2. Yo _____ lavo.
3. Ella _____ levanta a las ocho.
4. Ella _____ levanta al niño.
5. Él _____ mira la televisión.
6. Él _____ mira en el espejo.

L   Answer the following questions.

1. ¿Cómo te llamas?

_____

2. ¿A qué hora te levantas?

_____

3. ¿A qué hora te acuestas?

_____

4. En tu familia, ¿se acuestan todos Uds. a la misma hora?

_____

5. ¿Se viste tu madre o tu padre antes o después de tomar el desayuno?

_____

M   Choose the correct rejoinder or answer.

1. Me voy a lavar.
   - **a.** ¿Dónde está el champú?
   - **b.** ¿Dónde está el desodorante?
   - **c.** ¿Dónde está el jabón?

2. ¿Por qué quieres comprar un saco de dormir?
   - **a.** Porque voy a dormir.
   - **b.** Porque voy de camping.
   - **c.** Porque voy a un hotel.

3. ¿Quién trabaja en la tienda?
   - **a.** El dependiente.
   - **b.** El mesero.
   - **c.** El maletero.

4. ¿Por qué tienen equipaje?
   - **a.** Se visten.
   - **b.** Hacen un viaje.
   - **c.** Toman el tren.

5. ¿Tienen que transbordar los pasajeros?
   - **a.** Sí, tienen que esperar el tren.
   - **b.** Sí, tienen que subir al tren.
   - **c.** Sí, tienen que cambiar de tren.

6. ¿Van a dejar una propina grande?
   - **a.** No, porque el mesero les sirvió muy bien.
   - **b.** No, porque pagan con una tarjeta de crédito.
   - **c.** No, no es necesario. El servicio está incluído.

Answers appear on pages 180–181.

ANSWERS TO SELF-TEST 1

If you made any mistakes on the test, review the corresponding page(s) in your textbook indicated in parentheses under the answers to that section of the test.

A

1. d	**4.** g	**7.** h
2. f	**5.** b	**8.** c
3. a	**6.** e	

(For questions 1–3, 6, 8, review Chapter 1, *Palabras 1,* pages 14–15. For questions 4–5, review Chapter 2, *Palabras 2,* pages 40–41. For question 7, review Chapter 3, *Palabras 1,* pages 66–67.)

B

1. la escuela
2. el bus escolar
3. el libro
4. el examen
5. la pizarra (el pizarrón)
6. el refresco
7. el disco
8. el teléfono

(For questions 1–3, 6, 8, review Chapter 3, *Palabras 1,* pages 66–67. For questions 4–5, review Chapter 3, *Palabras 2,* pages 69–70. For questions 6–8, review Chapter 4, *Palabras 1,* pages 90–91.)

C

1. por teléfono
2. discos
3. un(a) alumno(a) serio(a)
4. una fiesta
5. un examen (una merienda)
6. en una tienda
7. en autobús (a las ocho)
8. la lección
9. a las ocho (en autobús)
10. la televisión
11. el piano
12. el tango
13. una merienda

(For questions 1–2, 10, review Chapter 4, *Palabras 1,* pages 90–91. For questions 3, 5, 8, review Chapter 3, *Palabras 2,* pages 69–70. For questions 4, 11-13, review Chapter 4, *Palabras 2,* pages 94–95. For questions 6–7, 9, review Chapter 3, *Palabras 1,* pages 66–67.)

D

1. Yo soy ____.	**5.** Yo llego a la escuela a las ____.
2. Yo soy ____.	**6.** Yo voy a ____.
3. Yo hablo ____.	**7.** Yo estoy ____.
4. Yo tomo ____.	

(For questions 1–2, review Chapter 1, *El presente del verbo ser, Formas singulares,* page 25. For questions 3-5, review Chapter 3, *El presente de los verbos en –ar, Formas singulares,* page 73. For questions 6-7, review Chapter 4, *El presente de los verbos ir, dar y estar,* page 100.)

E

1. son	**7.** es
2. somos	**8.** estamos
3. vamos	**9.** escuchan, hablan, toman
4. llegas	
5. tomas	**10.** voy
6. estudio	**11.** dan

(For questions 1–2, review Chapter 2, *El presente del verbo ser, Formas plurales,* page 50. For questions 3, 8, 10–11, review Chapter 4, *El presente de los verbos ir, dar y estar,* page 100. For questions 4–6, review Chapter 3, *El presente de los verbos en –ar, Formas singulares,* page 73. For question 7, review Chapter 1, *El presente del verbo ser, Formas singulares,* page 25. For question 9, review Chapter 4, *El presente de los verbos en –ar, Formas plurales,* page 98.)

F

1. El muchacho es alto.
2. Las muchachas son sinceras.
3. Los cursos son interesantes.
4. La profesora es amable.
5. Las clases son grandes.
6. Los hermanos son populares.
7. La lección es difícil.

(For questions 1, 4, 7, review Chapter 1, *La concordancia de los adjetivos, Formas singulares,* page 24 and Chapter 2, *El presente del verbo ser, Formas singulares,* page 25. For questions 2–3, 5–6, review Chapter 2, *Los sustantivos, artículos y adjetivos, Formas plurales,* page 48 and Chapter 3, *El presente del verbo ser, Formas plurales,* page 50.)

G

1. a la	**4.** del
2. de las, al	**5.** de los
3. a la	

(Review Chapter 4, *Las contracciones* al *y* del, page 102.)

H

1. b	**4.** c
2. c	**5.** a
3. a	**6.** b

(For question 1, review Chapter 1, *Lectura y cultura,* page 30. For questions 2–3, review Chapter 2, *Lectura y cultura,* page 56. For question 4, review Chapter 3, *Lectura y cultura,* page 80. For question 5, review Chapter 4, *Lectura y cultura,* page 106. For question 6, review Chapter 4, *Palabras 2,* pages 90–91.)

ANSWERS TO SELF-TEST 2

If you made any mistakes on the test, review the corresponding page(s) in your textbook indicated in parentheses under the answers to that section of the test.

A

1. el dormitorio, el comedor, la sala (el cuarto de baño, la habitación, el cuarto de dormir, la cocina)
2. casa
3. calle
4. come, toma (bebe)
5. periódico, bolígrafo (lápiz)
6. parque (jardín), flores
7. carro (coche)
8. deportes
9. campo
10. portero, equipo, tanto

(For questions 1–3, review Chapter 5, *Palabras 1,* pages 128-129. For questions 4–5, review Chapter 5, *Palabras 2,* pages 132–133. For questions 6–7, review Chapter 6, *Palabras 2,* pages 157–158. For questions 8–10, review Chapter 7, *Palabras 1,* pages 180–181.)

B

1. mi hermano	**3.** mi tío
2. mi abuela	**4.** mi primo

(Review Chapter 6, *Palabras 1,* pages 154–155.)

C

1. el mostrador	**4.** la tarjeta de embarque
2. el boleto (el billete)	**5.** el maletero (la maletera)
3. el asistente de vuelo	

(For question 3, review Chapter 8, *Palabras 1,* pages 206–207. For questions 1–2, 4–5, review Chapter 8, *Palabras 2,* page 210.)

D

1. veo	**7.** tenemos
2. comemos	**8.** tiene
3. vivimos	**9.** hago
4. recibo	**10.** pone
5. leen	**11.** salgo
6. tengo	**12.** salimos

(For questions 1–5, review Chapter 5, *El presente de los verbos en –er e –ir,* page 136. For questions 6–8, review Chapter 6, *El presente del verbo* tener, page 161. For questions 9–12, review *El presente de los verbos* hacer, poner, traer, salir *y* venir, page 214.)

E

1. empezamos ahora	**5.** volvemos ahora
2. quieren salir	**6.** preferimos comer ahora
3. pueden	
4. juega bien	**7.** duerme ocho horas

(For questions 1–2, 6, review Chapter 7, *El presente de los verbos con el cambio* e > ie, page 187. For questions 3–5, 7, review Chapter 7, *El presente de los verbos con el cambio* o > ue, page 189.)

F

1. Mi	**4.** Sus, mis
2. Su	**5.** tus, tu
3. Nuestra	

(Review Chapter 6, *Los adjetivos posesivos,* page 165.)

G

1. Ellos están saliendo ahora.
2. Estoy haciendo el viaje con ellos.
3. Estamos viajando en avión.
4. Yo estoy leyendo y él está escribiendo.
5. Los pasajeros están poniendo su equipaje en el compartimiento.
6. Tú estás reclamando las maletas.

(Review Chapter 8, *El presente progresivo,* page 218.)

H

1. Hay
2. tengo que
3. vamos a, tenemos que
4. tienen que, tienen que, va a

(For question 1, review Chapter 5, *La expresión impersonal* hay, page 141. For questions 2–4, review Chapter 6, Tener que + *el infinitivo,* Ir a + *el infinitivo,* page 163.)

I

1. F
2. T
3. T
4. T

5. F
6. F
7. T
8. F

(For questions 1–2, review Chapter 5, *Lectura y cultura*, page 144. For question 3, review Chapter 6, *Lectura y cultura*, page 170. For questions 4–5, review Chapter 7, *Lectura y cultura*, page196. For questions 6–8, review Chapter 8, *Lectura y cultura*, page 222.)

ANSWERS TO SELF-TEST 3

If you made any mistakes on the test, review the corresponding page(s) in your textbook indicated in parentheses under the answers to that section of the test.

A

1. el bastón
2. la pista
3. el gorro
4. los patines
5. la cama
6. la garganta
7. el médico

8. la receta
9. el traje de baño
10. los anteojos (las gafas) de sol
11. la plancha de vela
12. la piscina

(For questions 1–3, review Chapter 9, *Palabras 1*, pages 244–245. For question 4, review Chapter 9, *Palabras 2*, pages 248–249. For questions 5–6, review Chapter 10, *Palabras 1*, pages 270–271. For questions 7–8, review Chapter 10, *Palabras 2*, pages 274–275. For questions 9–11, review Chapter 11, *Palabras 1*, pages 296–297.For question 12, review Chapter 11, *Palabras 2*, pages 300–301.)

B

1. d
2. b
3. e
4. g
5. i

6. c
7. a
8. j
9. f
10. h

(For questions 1–3, 7, review Chapter 9, *Palabras 1*, pages 244–245. For question 4, review Chapter 9, *Palabras 2*, pages 248–249. For questions 5–6, review Chapter 10, *Palabras 1*, pages 270–271. For question 8, review Chapter 11, *Palabras 1*, pages 296–297. For question 9, review Chapter 11, *Palabras 2*, pages 300–301. For question 10, review Chapter 12, *Palabras 2*, pages 325–326.)

C

1. la pista
2. en el telesquí
3. enfermo
4. la gripe
5. la boca

6. medicamento, medicina
7. tenis
8. la cuenta
9. una propina
10. una película

(For questions 1–2, review Chapter 9, *Palabras 1*, pages 244–245. For questions 3–4, review Chapter 10, *Palabras 1*, pages 270–271. For questions 5–6, review Chapter 10, *Palabras 2*, pages 274–275. For question 7, review Chapter 11, *Palabras 2*, pages 300–301. For questions 8–9, review Chapter 12, *Palabras 2*, pages 325–326. For question 10, review Chapter 12, *Palabras 1*, pages 322–323.)

D

1. nadan, invierno
2. esquiadores, telesquí
3. catarro
4. cabeza
5. abre, garganta
6. receta, farmacéutico
7. sol, nublado
8. metro

(For questions 1–2, review Chapter 9, *Palabras 1*, pages 244–245. For questions 3–4, review Chapter 10, *Palabras 1*, pages 270–271. For questions 5–6, review Chapter 10, *Palabras 2*, pages 274–275. For question 7, review Chapter 11, *Palabras 1*, pages 296–297. For question 8, review Chapter 12, *Palabras 1*, pages 322–323.)

E

1. conozco
2. sé

3. sabe
4. sé, conoce

(Review Chapter 9, *El presente de los verbos* saber y conocer, page 252.)

F

1. está
2. es
3. es
4. es

5. está
6. es
7. está

(Review Chapter 10, *Ser y estar*, page 278.)

G

1. digo
2. dice

3. decimos
4. dicen

(Review Chapter 9, *El presente del verbo* decir, page 255.)

H

1. Te	**4.** la
2. nos	**5.** lo
3. le	**6.** las

(For questions 1–2, review Chapter 10, *Los pronombres me, te, nos*, page 283. For question 3, review Chapter 12, *Los complementos indirectos le, les*, page 332. For questions 4–6, review Chapter 11, *Los pronombres de complemento directo*, page 307.)

I

1. Yo nadé en el mar.
2. Mis amigos bucearon.
3. ¿Alquilaste un barco?
4. ¿Tomaron Uds. el sol?
5. ¿Usaste una crema protectora?
6. Ellos subieron la montaña en el telesquí.
7. Yo perdí mis gafas.
8. ¿Comiste mucho?
9. ¿Quién te dio las lecciones?
10. Vi la película.
11. Jugué (al) fútbol.
12. Ya empecé.

(For questions 1–5, 11–12, review Chapter 11, *El pretérito de los verbos en –ar*, page 304. For questions 6–10, review Chapter 12, *El pretérito de los verbos en –er e –ir*, page 329.)

J

1. c	**4.** a
2. c	**5.** b
3. a	

(For questions 1–3, review Chapter 9, *Lectura y cultura*, page 260. For questions 4–5, review Chapter 12, *Descubrimiento cultural*, page 340.)

K

1. F	**3.** T
2. T	**4.** T

(For questions 1–2, review Chapter 10, *Lectura y cultura*, page 286. For question 3, review Chapter 9, *Descubrimiento cultural*, pages 262-263. For question 4, review Chapter 11, *Lectura cultural*, page 312.)

ANSWERS TO SELF-TEST 4

If you made any mistakes on the test, review the corresponding page(s) in your textbook indicated in parentheses under the answers to that section of the test.

A

1. los tenis	**6.** el precio
2. la falda	**7.** la gabardina
3. la camisa	**8.** el suéter
4. el cinturón	**9.** los pantalones
5. la talla (el tamaño)	

(Review Chapter 13, *Palabras 1*, pages 360–361.)

B

1. pasajeros	**4.** quiosco
2. ventanilla (taquilla)	**5.** maletero (mozo)
3. ida y vuelta	

(Review Chapter 14, *Palabras 1*, pages 386–387.)

C

1. el cuchillo	**4.** el plato
2. el tenedor	**5.** el vaso
3. la cucharita	**6.** la taza

(Review Chapter 15, *Palabras 1*, pages 410–411.)

D

1. barra (pastilla)	**3.** se levanta
2. peine	**5.** se cepilla

(For questions 1–2, review Chapter 16, *Palabras 2*, pages 438–439. For questions 3–4, review Chapter 16, *Palabras 1*, pages 434–435.)

E

1. estrecho	**8.** tarde (con una demora, un retraso)
2. bajo	
3. largo	**9.** las legumbres
4. blanco	**10.** bien hecho
5. la salida	**11.** estar de pie
6. ocupado	**12.** despertarse
7. subir al tren	**13.** tarde
	14. barato

(For questions 1–4, review Chapter 13, *Palabras 2*, pages 364–365. For question 5, review Chapter 14, *Palabras 1*, page 386–387. For questions 6–8, 11, 13, review Chapter 14, *Palabras 2*, pages 390–391. For questions 9–10, review Chapter 15, *Palabras 2*, pages 414–415. For question 12, review Chapter 16, *Palabras 1*, pages 434–435. For question 14, review Chapter 13, *Palabras 1*, pages 360–361.)

F

1. Voy a comprar esta camisa porque me gusta.
2. Ellos van a comprar la raqueta porque les gusta.
3. Vas a comprar el blue jean porque te gusta.
4. Ellos van a comprar los tenis porque les gustan.
5. Yo voy a comprar los zapatos porque me gustan.
6. Vamos a comprar el disco porque nos gusta.

(Review Chapter 13, *El verbo* gustar, page 369.)

G

1. No tiene nada.
2. Ella no ve a nadie en la sala.
3. Ellos nunca viajan. (Ellos no viajan nunca.)
4. Yo no viajo tampoco.
5. ¿No tienes ni lápiz ni bolígrafo?

(Review Chapter 13, *Las palabras negativas y afirmativas*, page 372.)

H

1. quiso	5. Pusiste
2. hicieron	6. anduvimos
3. pude	7. estuvieron
4. vinieron	8. vine

(For questions 1–2, 4, 8, review Chapter 14, *El pretérito de los verbos* hacer, querer *y* venir, page 394. For questions 3, 5–7, review Chapter 14, *El pretérito de otros verbos irregulares*, page 396.)

I

1. pido	4. pedimos
2. pide	5. pedimos
3. sirve	

(Review Chapter 15, *El presente de los verbos con el cambio* e > i, page 418.)

J

1. En el restaurante yo pedí un biftec.
2. Mi hermano lo pidió bien hecho.
3. El mesero nos sirvió.
4. Nosotros pedimos el plato otra vez.
5. Nosotros le pedimos la cuenta.

(Review Chapter 15, *El pretérito de los verbos con el cambio* e > i, o > u, page 420.)

K

1. –	4. –
2. me	5. –
3. se	6. se

(Review Chapter 15, *El presente de los verbos con el cambio* e > i, page 418.)

L

1. Yo me llamo _____.
2. Yo me levanto _____.
3. Yo me acuesto _____.
4. En nuestra familia, nosotros (no) nos acostamos a la misma hora.
5. Mi madre (Mi padre) se viste antes (después) de tomar el desayuno.

(For questions 1–2, review Chapter 16, *Los verbos reflexivos*, page 442. For questions 3–5, review Chapter 16, *Los verbos reflexivos de cambio radical*, page 446.)

M

1. c	4. b
2. b	5. c
3. a	6. c

(For questions 1–2 review Chapter 16, *Palabras 2*, pages 438–439. For question 3, review Chapter 13, *Palabras 1*, pages 360-361. For question 4, review Chapter 14, *Palabras 1*, pages 386–387. For question 5, review Chapter 14, *Palabras 2*, pages 390–391. For question 6, review Chapter 15, *Palabras 1*, pages 410-411.)

STUDENT TAPE MANUAL

STUDENT TAPE MANUAL

CONTENIDO

BIENVENIDOS

For all activities in the preliminary lessons A–H, you will be asked to listen or listen and repeat.

CAPÍTULO

1

UN AMIGO
UNA AMIGA

PRIMERA PARTE

VOCABULARIO

Palabras 1

Actividad A   Listen and repeat.

Actividad B   Listen and choose.

_____
Elena

_____
José Luis

_____
Bárbara

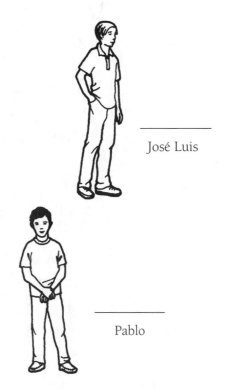

_____
Pablo

Palabras 2

Actividad C Listen and repeat.

Actividad D Listen and match.

a  **Colombia**

b  **México**

c **Puerto Rico**

d  **Cuba**

e **Chile**

f  **Estados Unidos**

1.	a	b	c	d	e	f	**6.**	a	b	c	d	e	f
2.	a	b	c	d	e	f	**7.**	a	b	c	d	e	f
3.	a	b	c	d	e	f	**8.**	a	b	c	d	e	f
4.	a	b	c	d	e	f	**9.**	a	b	c	d	e	f
5.	a	b	c	d	e	f	**10.**	a	b	c	d	e	f

ESTRUCTURA

Actividad A   Listen and choose.

a    b

1. a b	**5.** a b	**9.** a b
2. a b	**6.** a b	**10.** a b
3. a b	**7.** a b	**11.** a b
4. a b	**8.** a b	

Actividad B   Listen and choose.

1. sí no	**3.** sí no	**5.** sí no
2. sí no	**4.** sí no	**6.** sí no

Actividad C   Listen.

Actividad D   Listen and choose.

1. **a.** María   **b.** Marta   **c.** Mónica

2. **a.** Marcos   **b.** Paco   **c.** Carlos

3. **a.** americana   **b.** mexicana   **c.** colombiana

4. **a.** los Estados Unidos   **b.** México   **c.** Colombia

CONVERSACIÓN

Actividad E   Listen.

Actividad F   Listen and choose.

1. **a.** Davis   **b.** Torres   **c.** Figueroa

2. **a.** Inés   **b.** Maricarmen   **c.** la señora Torres

3. **a.** antipática   **b.** americana   **c.** sincera

4. **a.** los Estados Unidos **b.** México   **c.** Colombia

5. **a.** Inés   **b.** David   **c.** Maricarmen

PRONUNCIACIÓN

Actividad G   Pronunciación: *Las vocales* a, o y u

When you speak Spanish, it is very important to pronounce the vowels carefully. The vowel sounds in Spanish are very short, clear, and concise. The vowels in English have several different pronunciations, but in Spanish they have only one sound. Imitate carefully the pronunciation of the vowels *a*, *o*, and *u*. Note that the pronunciation of *a* is similar to the *a* in *father*, *o* is similar to the *o* in *most*, and *u* is similar to the *u* in *flu*. Listen and repeat after the speaker.

SEGUNDA PARTE

Actividad A   Listen and choose.

1. **a.** colombiana   **b.** puertorriqueña   **c.** mexicana

2. **a.** Santiago   **b.** Santa Teresa   **c.** Ramona

3. **a.** Colombia   **b.** Puerto Rico   **c.** México

4. **a.** baja y morena   **b.** alta y rubia   **c.** alta y morena

Actividad B   Listen and choose.

1. a   b   c   3. a   b   c   5. a   b   c

2. a   b   c   4. a   b   c   6. a   b   c

Actividad C   Listen and choose.

_____   _____   _____

_____   _____   _____

_____   _____   _____

Actividad D   Listen and choose.

_____

Sara Cortés

_____

Abelardo Vega

_____

Susana Martín

_____

José Luis Peña

_____

Carmen Mercado

_____

Ignacio Funes

_____

Roberto Rojas

_____

David Oliver

CAPÍTULO

2

¿HERMANOS O AMIGOS?

PRIMERA PARTE

VOCABULARIO

Palabras 1

Actividad A Listen and repeat.

Actividad B Listen and choose.

a  b

1. a b		**3.** a b		**5.** a b		**7.** a b	
2. a b		**4.** a b		**6.** a b		**8.** a b	

Actividad C Listen and match.

_____ intelligent   _____ interesting   _____ serious

_____ important   _____ popular

Actividad D Listen and answer.

Palabras 2

Actividad E Listen and repeat.

Nombre _____ Fecha _____

Actividad F Listen and choose.

1. **a.** aritmética   **b.** biología   **c.** historia

2. **a.** álgebra   **b.** arte   **c.** francés

3. **a.** trigonometría   **b.** química   **c.** inglés

4. **a.** geografía   **b.** aritmética   **c.** latín

5. **a.** sociología   **b.** física   **c.** italiano

6. **a.** biología   **b.** educación física   **c.** español

7. **a.** educación cívica   **b.** economía doméstica   **c.** arte

ESTRUCTURA

Actividad A Listen and choose.

1. a   b   c   5. a   b   c

2. a   b   c   6. a   b   c

3. a   b   c   7. a   b   c

4. a   b   c

Actividad B Listen.

Actividad C Listen and answer.

Actividad D Listen and choose.

_____

_____

_____

_____

_____

_____

STUDENT TAPE MANUAL

CONVERSACIÓN

Actividad E   Listen.

Actividad F   Listen and choose.

1.   **a.** Coyoacán   **b.** Arlington   **c.** la Ciudad de México

2.   **a.** una ciudad grande   **b.** una capital   **c.** un suburbio

3.   **a.** Wáshington   **b.** Coyoacán   **c.** Arlington

4.   **a.** Wáshington   **b.** Coyoacán   **c.** la Ciudad de México

5.   **a.** una ciudad   **b.** un suburbio   **c.** un país

PRONUNCIACIÓN

Actividad G   Pronunciación: *Las vocales* e *e* i

The sounds of the Spanish vowels *e* and *i* are short, clear, and concise. The pronunciation of *e* is similar to the *a* in *mate* and the pronunciation of *i* is similar to the *ee* in *bee* or *see*. Listen and repeat after the speaker.

SEGUNDA PARTE

Actividad A   Listen and choose.

1.   **a.** álgebra   **b.** geometría   **c.** química

2.   **a.** música   **b.** trigonometría   **c.** arte

3.   **a.** biología   **b.** español   **c.** historia

4.   **a.** geografía   **b.** educación cívica   **c.** aritmética

5.   **a.** química   **b.** arte   **c.** historia

6.   **a.** música   **b.** sociología   **c.** educación física

7.   **a.** inglés   **b.** física   **c.** geografía

8.   **a.** biología   **b.** economía doméstica **c.** arte

Actividad B   Look, listen, and answer.

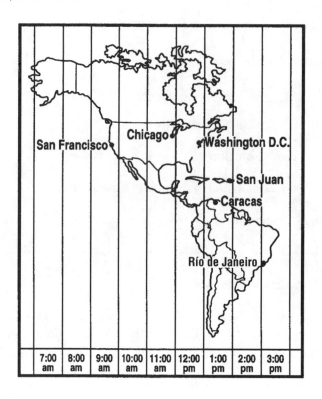

Actividad C   Listen and choose.

José Luis

1.   Córdoba / Cochabamba

2.   Bolivia / Venezuela

3.   alumno / profesor

4.   escuela pública / colegio privado

5.   matemáticas / arte

6.   fabuloso / aburrido

Pilar

1.   Bolivia / Venezuela

2.   Caracas / La Paz

3.   Caracas / La Paz

4.   profesora / alumna

5.   las ciencias / las lenguas

Doña Flor

1.   alumna / profesora

2.   matemáticas / ciencias

3.   biología y física / álgebra y geometría

4.   Colombia / Perú

5.   Lima / Bogotá

6.   fáciles / difíciles

Actividad D Listen and answer.

1. What have they just inaugurated?

   _____

2. It is a public or private school?

   _____

3. Is it for boys or for girls?

   _____

4. What might be "asignaturas típicas"?

   _____

5. What is the specialty in mechanics?

   _____

6. There is a separate department for what?

   _____

CAPÍTULO

3

EN LA ESCUELA

PRIMERA PARTE

VOCABULARIO

Palabras 1

Actividad A   Listen and repeat.

Actividad B   Listen and choose.

_____   _____   _____

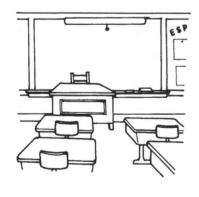

_____   _____   _____

Actividad C   Listen and choose.

  1. sí   no   **2.** sí   no   **3.** sí   no   **4.** sí   no   **5.** sí   no

Palabras 2

Actividad D Listen and repeat.

Actividad E Listen and complete.

Actividad F Listen and choose.

    1. a b c   **5.** a b c

    2. a b c   **6.** a b c

    3. a b c   **7.** a b c

    4. a b c

Actividad G Listen and write.

Example: *(You hear)*   Roberto llega a las ocho.
                             ¿Quién?
                (You write)   Roberto

Example: *(You hear)*   Roberto llega a las ocho.
                             ¿Cuándo?
                (You write)   a las ocho

    1. _____   **4.** _____

    2. _____   **5.** _____

    3. _____   **6.** _____

ESTRUCTURA

Actividad A Listen and answer.

Actividad B Listen and answer.

Actividad C Listen and confirm.

Example: *(You hear)* Estudio latín.
                (You say)   ¿Qué estudias?

Actividad D Listen and confirm.

Example: *(You hear)* Estudio inglés.
                (You say)   Elena estudia inglés.

Actividad E Listen and choose.

a    b

1. a b   **3.** a b   **5.** a b

2. a b   **4.** a b

Actividad F Listen and choose.

1. sí no   **3.** sí no   **5.** sí no   **7.** sí no

2. sí no   **4.** sí no   **6.** sí no   **8.** sí no

CONVERSACIÓN

Actividad G Listen.

Actividad H Listen and answer.

PRONUNCIACIÓN

Actividad I Pronunciación: *Las consonantes* l, f, p, m, n

The pronunciation of the consonants *l, f, p, m,* and *n* is quite similar in both Spanish and English. However, the *p* is not followed by a puff of breath as it often is in English. When you make the *p* sound in Spanish you round your lips. Listen and repeat after the speaker.

SEGUNDA PARTE

Actividad A Listen and choose.

1. a b   **5.** a b

2. a b   **6.** a b

3. a b   **7.** a b

4. a b

Actividad B   Look, listen, and answer.

	CURSO	DOCENTE	SALON
8:00–8:50	Historia de Europa	Sra. Alvarado Guzmán	122
9:00–9:50	Geometría	Dra. Figueroa Simón	306
10:00–10:50	Estudio individual		Teatro
11:00–11:50	Literatura	Sr. Morales Cuadra	123
11:50–14:00	Almuerzo		Cafetería
14:00–14:50	Inglés	Sr. Linares Clark	249
15:00–15:50	Química	Srta. Reyes Olivares	231
16:00–16:50	Deportes	Sr. Campos Ruiz	Gimnasio

Example: *(You hear)*   La doctora Figueroa es una profesora excelente.
          (You also hear)   ¿De qué curso habla Manuel?
          (You write)   Geometría.

1. _____
2. _____
3. _____
4. _____
5. _____

6. _____
7. _____
8. _____
9. _____
10. _____

Actividad C   Listen and choose.

_____	Andrés Jiménez Gaona	**a.**	Ecuador
_____	Beatriz Campos	**b.**	Chile
_____	Luisa Rodríguez Campoamor	**c.**	España
_____	Ramona Carrillo Mackenna	**d.**	México
_____	Jorge Muñoz Franco	**e.**	Costa Rica
_____	Susana Huidobro	**f.**	Puerto Rico
_____	Antonio Villegas Luna	**g.**	Venezuela
_____	Teresa Mendizábal	**h.**	Colombia

CAPÍTULO 4

PASATIEMPOS
DESPUÉS DE LAS CLASES

PRIMERA PARTE

VOCABULARIO

Palabras 1

Actividad A Listen and repeat.

Actividad B Listen and choose.

_____ _____ _____

_____ _____ _____

Actividad C   Listen and choose.

1.   **a.** la biblioteca   **b.** la sala

2.   **a.** el disco   **b.** la tienda

3.   **a.** la cocina   **b.** la biblioteca

4.   **a.** la biblioteca   **b.** la cocina

5.   **a.** el centro comercial   **b.** la casa

6.   **a.** la casa   **b.** el centro comercial

Actividad D   Listen and choose.

1. sí   no   3. sí   no   5. sí   no   7. sí   no

2. sí   no   4. sí   no   6. sí   no   8. sí   no

Palabras 2

Actividad E   Listen and repeat.

Actividad F   Listen.

Actividad G   Listen and choose.

1.   **a.** una merienda   **b.** una guitarra   **c.** una fiesta

2.   **a.** a los hermanos   **b.** a los amigos   **c.** a la profesora

3.   **a.** en un café   **b.** en casa   **c.** en una clase

4.   **a.** No, no cantan.   **b.** Sí, y también estudian. **c.** Sí, y también bailan.

5.   **a.** el violín   **b.** el piano   **c.** la trompeta

6.   **a.** María   **b.** José   **c.** los muchachos

7.   **a.** refrescos   **b.** una merienda   **c.** café

Actividad H   Listen and answer.

Actividad I   Listen and answer.

Example: *(You hear)*   ¿Pablo escucha el violín?
           (You see)   tocar
           (You say)   No, Pablo toca el violín.

1. bailar   3. estudiar   5. mirar la televisión

2. tomar   4. trabajar   6. escuchar

ESTRUCTURA

Actividad A   Listen and choose.

1. a   b   c   4. a   b   c   7. a   b   c

2. a   b   c   5. a   b   c   8. a   b   c

3. a   b   c   6. a   b   c

Actividad B   Listen and answer.

1. fiesta   5. sí

2. a pie   6. Sara

3. Marta y Sara   7. bien

4. en casa

Actividad C   Listen and choose.

una fiesta   la sala   la clase

la cocina   el autobús   el laboratorio

CONVERSACIÓN

Actividad D   Listen.

Actividad E   Listen and choose.

1. **a.** bien   **b.** mal

2. **a.** en una fiesta   **b.** en una tienda

3. **a.** Clarita   **b.** María

4. **a.** en una tienda de libros **b.** en una tienda de discos

5. **a.** Clarita   **b.** María

6. **a.** después del trabajo   **b.** no van

PRONUNCIACIÓN

Actividad F   Pronunciación: *La consonante* t

The *t* in Spanish is pronounced with the tip of the tongue pressed against the upper teeth. Like the Spanish *p*, it is not followed by a puff of air. The Spanish *t* is extremely clear. Listen and repeat after the speaker.

SEGUNDA PARTE

Actividad A   Listen.

Actividad B   Listen and choose.

1.   **a.** Mercedes   **b.** Jorge   **c.** Leonor

2.   **a.** Mercedes   **b.** Jorge   **c.** Leonor

3.   **a.** Mercedes   **b.** Jorge   **c.** Leonor

4.   **a.** a la tienda   **b.** a casa   **c.** a la biblioteca

5.   **a.** Mercedes   **b.** Jorge   **c.** Leonor

6.   **a.** a casa de Jorge   **b.** a casa de Leonor   **c.** a clase

7.   **a.** para estudiar   **b.** para mirar la televisión   **c.** para bailar

8.   **a.** la casa de Leonor **b.** la tienda   **c.** la escuela

9.   **a.** 4   **b.** 14   **c.** 40

10. **a.** Mercedes   **b.** Jorge   **c.** Leonor

11. **a.** 3:00   **b.** 3:30   **c.** 4:00

12. **a.** discos   **b.** una merienda   **c.** refrescos

13. **a.** discos   **b.** una merienda   **c.** refrescos

Actividad C   Listen.

Actividad D   Listen and choose.

1. a b c	5. a b c	9. a b c
2. a b c	6. a b c	10. a b c
3. a b c	7. a b c	11. a b c
4. a b c	8. a b c	

Actividad E   Listen and choose.

| 1. sí   no | 3. sí   no | 5. sí   no | 7. sí   no | 9. sí   no |
| 2. sí   no | 4. sí   no | 6. sí   no | 8. sí   no | 10. sí   no |

Actividad F Listen and match.

a

b

c

d

e

f

g

h

1. _____ Pablo

2. _____ María

3. _____ Susana

4. _____ Roberto

5. _____ Beatriz

6. _____ Fernando

7. _____ Elena

8. _____ Carlos

Actividad G   Look, listen, and answer.

1.   Is the job full-time or part-time?

_____

2.   What is the name of the store?

_____

3.   Do they want a boy or a girl?

_____

4.   How old must the worker be?

_____

5.   Where is the store located?

_____

6.   What do they sell at the store?

_____

7   How can a person get in touch with the owner?

_____

8.   What is the owner's name?

_____

9.   What is her phone number?

_____

10.   What days can she be called on the phone?

_____

11.   Between what hours can she be called?

_____

CAPÍTULO
5

ACTIVIDADES DEL HOGAR

PRIMERA PARTE

VOCABULARIO

Palabras 1

Actividad A   Listen and repeat.

Actividad B   Listen and repeat.

Actividad C   Listen.

Actividad D   Listen and choose.

1. sí   no   **2.** sí   no   **3.** sí   no   **4.** sí   no   **5.** sí   no

Actividad E   Listen and choose.

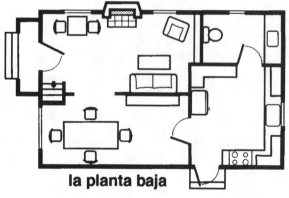

la planta baja   **el primer piso**

1.   **a.** cuatro   **b.** seis

2.   **a.** cuatro   **b.** cinco

3.   **a.** planta baja   **b.** primer piso

4.   **a.** planta baja   **b.** primer piso

5.   **a.** planta baja   **b.** primer piso

6.   **a.** planta baja   **b.** primer piso

Palabras 2

Actividad F   Listen and repeat.

Actividad G   Listen and choose.

_____   _____   _____

Actividad H   Listen and repeat.

Actividad I   Listen and choose.

_____   _____   _____

_____   _____   _____

Actividad J   Listen and repeat.

Actividad K   Listen and choose.

_____   _____   _____

Actividad L   Listen and repeat.

Actividad M   Listen and choose.

_____   _____   _____

Actividad N   Listen and repeat.

Actividad O   Listen and choose.

_____   _____   _____

Actividad P   Listen and repeat.

Actividad Q   Listen and choose.

_____   _____   _____

Actividad R Listen and repeat.

Actividad S Listen and choose.

1. siempre   a veces   4. siempre   a veces

2. siempre   a veces   5. siempre   a veces

3. siempre   a veces

ESTRUCTURA

Actividad A Listen and answer.

Actividad B Listen and choose.

1. a   b   c   3. a   b   c   5. a   b   c

2. a   b   c   4. a   b   c   6. a   b   c

CONVERSACIÓN

Actividad C Listen.

Actividad D Listen and choose.

1. sí   no   5. sí   no

2. sí   no   6. sí   no

3. sí   no   7. sí   no

4. sí   no

PRONUNCIACIÓN

Actividad E Pronunciación: *La consonante* d

The pronunciation of the consonant *d* in Spanish varies according to its position in the word. When a word begins with *d* (initial position) or follows the consonants *l* or *n*, the tongue gently strikes the back of the upper front teeth. Listen and repeat after the speaker.

When *d* appears within the word between vowels (medial position), the *d* is extremely soft. To pronounce this *d* properly, your tongue should strike the lower part of your upper teeth, almost between the upper and lower teeth. Listen and repeat after the speaker.

When a word ends in *d* (final position), the *d* is either extremely soft or omitted completely, not pronounced. Listen and repeat after the speaker.

SEGUNDA PARTE

Actividad A   Listen.

Actividad B   Listen and choose.

      1. a   b   **2.** a   b   **3.** a   b

Actividad C   Listen and choose.

      1. 1 2 3 4 5 6 7 8 9

      2. 1 2 3 4 5 6 7 8 9

      3. 1 2 3 4 5 6 7 8 9

      4. 1 2 3 4 5 6 7 8 9

      5. 1 2 3 4 5 6 7 8 9

      6. 1 2 3 4 5 6 7 8 9

Actividad D   Listen and choose.

_____   _____   _____

_____   _____   _____

Actividad E   Look, listen, and choose.

1.   What is the client's name?

   a. San Martín   **b.** Villa   **c.** Providencia

2.   Where does he want to live?

   a. downtown   **b.** in the suburbs   **c.** in the country

3.   What is he looking for?

   a. a small apartment   **b.** a large apartment   **c.** a private house

4.   How many houses does the realtor say are available downtown?

   a. none   **b.** a few   **c.** many

5.   How many children does the family have?

   a. 3   **b.** 6   **c.** 8

6.   Who else lives with the family?

   a. the man's father   **b.** the wife's mother   **c.** a maid

7.   How many bedrooms does the place suggested have?

   a. 4   **b.** 6   **c.** 8

8.   What is nearby?

   a. a school   **b.** a restaurant   **c.** a metro stop

9.   How many floors does the building have?

   a. 3   **b.** 6   **c.** 8

10.   On what floors are the bedrooms?

   a. 1 and 2   **b.** 2 and 3   **c.** 3 and 4

11.   Where is the building in relation to the metro?

   a. in front   **b.** to the left   **c.** to the right

12.   Where are the man and woman going now?

   a. to the bank   **b.** to the metro   **c.** to the house

LA FAMILIA Y SU CASA

PRIMERA PARTE

VOCABULARIO

Palabras 1

Actividad A   Listen and repeat.

Actividad B   Listen and choose.

1. sí   no   3. sí   no   5. sí   no   7. sí   no   9. sí   no

2. sí   no   4. sí   no   6. sí   no   8. sí   no   10. sí   no

Actividad C Listen and choose.

1. **a.** tío   **b.** hermano   **c.** abuelo

2. **a.** tío   **b.** primo   **c.** sobrino

3. **a.** tía   **b.** prima   **c.** sobrina

4. **a.** abuelos   **b.** primos   **c.** sobrinos

5. **a.** prima   **b.** sobrina   **c.** tía

6. **a.** abuelo   **b.** sobrino   **c.** tío

7. **a.** abuela   **b.** tía   **c.** prima

8. **a.** sobrino   **b.** abuelo   **c.** tío

9. **a.** tíos   **b.** abuelos   **c.** sobrinos

Palabras 2

Actividad D Listen and repeat.

Actividad E Listen and choose.

_____   _____   _____

_____   _____

ESTRUCTURA

Actividad A Listen.

Actividad B Listen and choose.

    1. sí no **2.** sí no **3.** sí no **4.** sí no **5.** sí no

Actividad C Listen and choose.

    1. a b c   **3.** a b c   **5.** a b c

    2. a b c   **4.** a b c   **6.** a b c

Actividad D Listen and answer.

Actividad E Listen and answer.

    Example: (*You hear*) Pablo va a estudiar.
              (*You see*) trabajar
              (*You say*) No, Pablo va a trabajar.

    1. buenas notas   **3.** una película   **5.** una "A"

    2. un carro   **4.** dieciséis años   **6.** comprar

Actividad F Listen and answer.

    1. 8:00   **3.** 4:30   **5.** a la abuela

    2. el lunes   **4.** Teresa   **6.** una composición

Actividad G Listen and answer.

    Example: (*You hear*) ¿Vas a bailar?
              (*You see*) bailar / estudiar
              (*You say*) No, no voy a bailar porque tengo que estudiar.

    1. ver televisión / estudiar   **4.** escuchar discos / estudiar

    2. trabajar / estudiar   **5.** ir al café / estudiar

    3. comprar regalos / estudiar   **6.** preparar unos refrescos / estudiar

Actividad H Listen and answer.

    Example: (*You hear*) ¿Es el libro de Laura?
              (*You say*) Sí, es su libro.

CONVERSACIÓN

Actividad I   Listen.

Actividad J   Listen and choose.

   1. a   b   **2.** a   b   **3.** a   b   **4.** a   b

PRONUNCIACIÓN

Actividad K   Pronunciación: *Las consonantes* b, v

There is no difference in pronunciation between a *b* and a *v* in Spanish. The *b* or *v* sound is somewhat softer than the sound of an English *b*. When making this sound, the lips barely touch. Listen and repeat after the speaker.

SEGUNDA PARTE

Actividad A   Listen.

Actividad B   Listen and choose.

   1. **a.** una escuela   **b.** un restaurante   **c.** un baile

   2. **a.** para celebrar y comer   **b.** para leer y escribir   **c.** para estudiar

   3. **a.** en las afueras de la ciudad **b.** en el centro de la ciudad   **c.** en un parque

   4. **a.** a 6 kilómetros   **b.** a 16 kilómetros   **c.** a 60 kilómetros

   5. **a.** en la planta baja   **b.** en los jardines   **c.** en la cocina

   6. **a.** 30   **b.** 50   **c.** 70

   7. **a.** la cocina   **b.** el comedor   **c.** el banquete

   8. **a.** dos   **b.** cuatro   **c.** ocho

   9. **a.** dos a tres   **b.** cuatro a ocho   **c.** seis a diez

   10. **a.** Montes   **b.** Ruano   **c.** Rojas

   11. **a.** una escuela   **b.** el Edificio Ruano   **c.** un jardín

   12. **a.** una escuela   **b.** el Edificio Ruano   **c.** un jardín

   13. **a.** lunes   **b.** martes   **c.** domingo

Actividad C   Look, listen, and choose.

1.   What is this ad for?

   a. a house   **b.** an apartment   **c.** a car

2.   Where is it located?

   a. in the mountains   **b.** in a garage   **c.** in downtown San Lucas

3.   What do the six thousand pesos cover?

   a. a month's rent   **b.** a year's repair and service   **c.** the total price

4.   What will happen Friday?

   a. The price will go up.   **b.** The offer will end.   **c.** The sale will begin.

5.   How many bedrooms are there?

   a. three   **b.** four   **c.** five

6.   How many bathrooms are there?

   a. one   **b.** two   **c.** three

7.   How many cars does the garage hold?

   a. one   **b.** two   **c.** three

8.   What can you see from the balcony?

   a. the park   **b.** the garden   **c.** the mountains

9.   What is the "Edificio Aguilar"?

   a. an automobile showroom   **b.** apartments   **c.** a restaurant

10.   What is the address of the "Edificio Aguilar"?

   a. calle San Lucas No.9   **b.** calle Sol No.77   **c.** calle Montaña No.4

11.   How old is the building?

   a. two years old   **b.** four years old   **c.** seven years old

12.   Does the building have an elevator?

   a. No, it doesn't.   **b.** Yes, one.   **c.** Yes, two.

Actividad D   Listen and ask.

Example: (*You hear*)   Voy a comprar un…
(*You say*)   ¿Cómo? ¿Qué vas a comprar?

Actividad E   Look, listen, and complete.

1. Javier is a famous _____

2. Today is Javier's _____

3. He is going to get a magnificent _____

4. "Los Cocodrilos" are Javier's _____

5. They are going to give him a _____

6. Tomorrow Javier is going to _____

7. Javier and "Los Cocodrilos" are going to be on _____

8. Javier will also be accompanied by _____

9. All his fans wish him _____

LOS DEPORTES DE EQUIPO

PRIMERA PARTE

VOCABULARIO

Palabras 1

Actividad A Listen and repeat.

Actividad B Listen and identify.

Actividad C Listen and repeat.

Actividad D   Listen and choose.

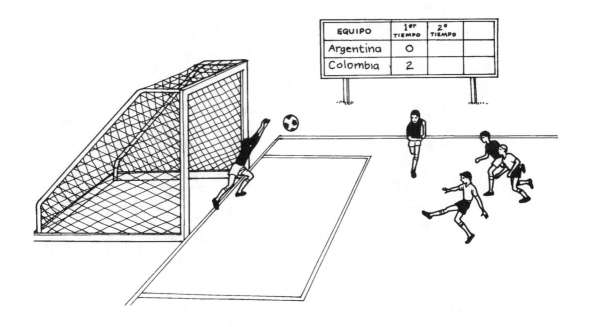

1. sí   no   **2.** sí   no   **3.** sí   no   **4.** sí   no   **5.** sí   no

Actividad E   Listen and choose.

1. a   b   c   **4.** a   b   c

2. a   b   c   **5.** a   b   c

3. a   b   c

Palabras 2

Actividad F   Listen and repeat.

Actividad G   Listen and choose.

_____   _____   _____

Actividad H   Listen and repeat.

Actividad I   Listen and identify.

Actividad J   Listen and repeat.

Actividad K   Listen and identify.

Actividad L   Listen and choose.

1. a	b	c	**5.** a	b	c	**8.** a	b	c
2. a	b	c	**6.** a	b	c	**9.** a	b	c
3. a	b	c	**7.** a	b	c	**10.** a	b	c
4. a	b	c						

ESTRUCTURA

Actividad A   Listen and answer.

Actividad B   Listen and answer.

1.

2.

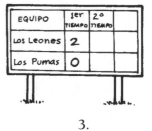

3.

4.

5.

6.

7.

8.

Actividad C Listen and answer.

1. Marta y Ramón
2. 3:30
3. Luis Sepúlveda
4. sí

5. los jugadores
6. el árbitro
7. el estadio
8. dos

Actividad D Listen and answer.

Example: (*You hear*) Juan es de España, ¿no?
(*You see*) México
(*You say*) No, no es español. Es mexicano.

1. España
2. Puerto Rico
3. Alemania
4. Nicaragua

5. Francia
6. Norteamérica
7. Argentina
8. Canadá

CONVERSACIÓN

Actividad E Listen.

Actividad F Listen and choose.

1. sí   no
2. sí   no
3. sí   no
4. sí   no

5. sí   no
6. sí   no
7. sí   no

PRONUNCIACIÓN

Actividad G Pronunciación: *Las consonantes* s, c, z

The consonant s is pronounced the same as the s in *sing*. Listen and repeat after the speaker.

The consonant c in combination with e or i (*ce, ci*) is pronounced the same as an s in all areas of Latin America. In many parts of Spain, *ce* and *ci* are pronounced *th*. Likewise the pronunciation of z in combination with a, o, u (*za, zo, zu*) is pronounced the same as an s throughout Latin America and as a *th* in most areas of Spain. Listen and repeat after the speaker.

SEGUNDA PARTE

Actividad A   Look, listen, and choose.

1.   Es un partido de _____.

   a. baloncesto   **b.** béisbol   **c.** fútbol

2.   Los dos equipos son Madrid y _____.

   a. Real   **b.** Barcelona   **c.** Vargas

3.   Quedan _____ minutos en el segundo tiempo.

   a. dos   **b.** tres   **c.** cinco

4.   Vargas lanza el balón con _____.

   a. la cabeza   **b.** el pie   **c.** la mano

5.   Meten un gol en el _____ minuto del partido.

   a. primer   **b.** tercer   **c.** último

6.   El resultado del partido es _____.

   a. una victoria para Madrid   **b.** un juego empatado   **c.** que Vargas pierde

Actividad B   Listen and choose.

   1. a   b   c   2. a   b   c   3. a   b   c

Actividad C   Look, listen, and choose.

Lanzadores Designados para Hoy

   Los siguientes son los lanzadores designados para abrir los partidos de hoy martes en el Béisbol de Grandes Ligas. La hora señalada corresponde al tiempo del este de Estados Unidos (cuatro horas menos que gmt).

Liga Americana

_____ California (Blyleven 9-2) en Toronto (Key 7-9), 7:35 p.m.

_____ Seattle (Johnson 3-1) en Baltimore (Ballard 10-4), 7:35 p.m.

_____ Oakland (Davis 7-4) en Detroit (Tanana 7-9), 7:35 p.m.

_____ Cleveland (Black 7-7) en Minnesota (Viola 7-10), 8:05 p.m.

_____ Nueva York (Hawkins 11-8) en Chicago (Reuss 7-5), 8:30 p.m.

_____ Milwaukee (August 9-7) en Kansas City (Gubicza 8-7), 8:35 p.m.

_____ Boston (Clemens 10-6) en Texas (Witt 7-8), 8:35 p.m.

Liga Nacional

_____ Houston (Clancy 5-6) en Nueva York (Fernández 7-3), 7:35 p.m.

_____ Atlanta (P.Smith 2-11) en Montreal (D. Martínez 10-1), 7:35 p.m.

_____ Filadelfia (Ruffin 3-3) en Cincinnati (Jackson 6-9), 7:35 p.m.

_____ Pittsburgh (Walk 7-5) en San Diego (Hurst 7-7), 10:05 p.m.

_____ San Luis (Hill 5-5) en San Francisco (D.Robinson 7-6), 10:35 p.m.

_____ Chicago (Maddux 9-7) en Los Angeles (Hershiser 10-7), 10:35 p.m.

CAPÍTULO 8

UN VIAJE EN AVIÓN

PRIMERA PARTE

VOCABULARIO

Palabras 1

Actividad A   Listen and repeat.

Actividad B   Listen and choose.

_____   _____   _____

_____   _____

Actividad C Listen and repeat.

Actividad D Look, listen, and answer.

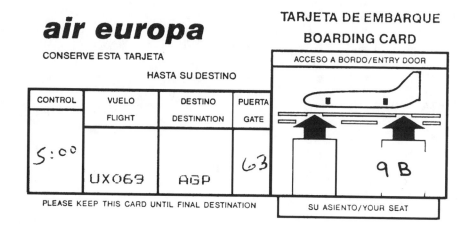

Actividad E Listen and choose.

1. a   b   c   3. a   b   c   5. a   b   c

2. a   b   c   4. a   b   c

Palabras 2

Actividad F Listen and repeat.

Actividad G Listen and choose.

_____   _____   _____

_____   _____

Actividad H Listen and choose.

1. sí no 2. sí no 3. sí no 4. sí no 5. sí no

Actividad I Listen and choose.

1. a b c   3. a b c   5. a b c

2. a b c   4. a b c   6. a b c

ESTRUCTURA

Actividad A Listen and answer.

1. sí   5. sí, libros

2. un viaje   6. refrescos

3. sí   7. a las cuatro

4. la ropa

Actividad B Listen and answer.

1. comer   5. traer los boletos

2. jugar al béisbol 6. venir al reclamo

3. enseñar   7. salir ahora

4. estudiar

Actividad C Listen and answer.

1. 3:00   3. 4:00   5. 5:00

2. 3:30   4. 4:30   6. 5:30

Actividad D Listen and answer.

Example: (You hear) ¿Habla Juan?
          (You say)   Sí, está hablando.

Actividad E Listen and answer.

Example: (You hear) Y ahora, ¿qué hace Juan?
          (You see)   comer
          (You say)   Está comiendo.

1. estudiar   4. aterrizar

2. trabajar   5. inspeccionar el equipaje

3. escribir   6. cerrar la maleta

CONVERSACIÓN

Actividad F   Listen.

Actividad G   Listen and choose.

1. a b c   5. a b c

2. a b c   6. a b c

3. a b c   7. a b c

4. a b c

PRONUNCIACIÓN

Actividad H   Pronunciación: *La consonante* c

You have already learned that *c* in combination with *e* or *i* (*ce, ci*) is pronounced like an s. The consonant *c* in combination with *a, o, u* (*ca, co, cu*) has a hard *k* sound. Listen and repeat after the speaker.

Since *ce, ci* have the soft s sound, *c* changes to *qu* when it combines with *e* or *i* (*que, qui*) in order to maintain the hard *k* sound. Listen and repeat after the speaker.

SEGUNDA PARTE

Actividad A   Listen and choose.

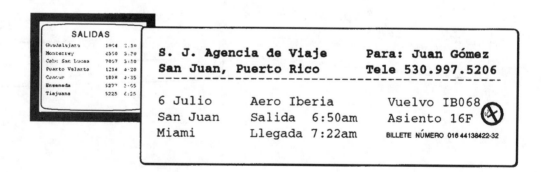

1. sí no   2. sí no   3. sí no   4. sí no   5. sí no

Actividad B Listen and answer.

G00977795   1

Este pasaporte contiene 32 páginas.
(CE PASSEPORT CONTIENT 32 PAGES)

DIEZ PESETAS

PASAPORTE-PAS___

ESPAÑA - ESPAGNE

SA Número 4.695/79
(NUMÉRO)

Nombre y Apellidos D. José Luis
(PRÉNOM ET NOMS)

Luis Rivas

Y de su esposa Dª
(ET DE SON ÉPOUSE)

Nacionalidad { Española de origen
(NATIONALITÉ)

2

Señas Personales.- (SIGNALEMENT)
Profesión   Estudiante
(PROFESSION)
Estado civil   Soltero
(ÉTAT CIVIL)
Lugar y fecha {   Málaga
de nacimiento {   19 agosto 1962
(LIEU ET DATE
DE NAISSANCE)

D. N. I. nº (CARTE D'IDENTITÉ) 7.852.466
Domicilio   Tejares
(DOMICILE)
Esposa (ÉPOUSE)
Lugar y fecha {
de nacimiento {
(LIEU ET DATE
DE NAISSANCE)

D. N. I. nº (CARTE D'IDENTITÉ)

Hijos Menores de 14 años
(ENFANTS DE MOINS DE 14 ANS)
Nombre (PRÉNOMS)   Edad (ÁGES)   Sexo (SEXE)

Actividad C Listen and answer.

Horario de vuelos

Llegadas internacionales a Guatemala

Guat.	Compañía	Vuelo	Equipo	Escalas Rutas
12:59	American	927	257	Miami/Guatemala
18:35		929	72M	Miami/Guatemala
20:33		991	72S	Dallas/Guatemala
06:30	Aviateca	961	733	Los Angeles/Guatemala
08:20		900	733	San José/MGA/Guatemala
08:40		021	733	Flores/Guatemala
15:30		911	73S	México/Guatemala
16:10		901	733	Miami/Guatemala
16:50		921	733	Houston/Mérida/Guatemala
16:40		023	733	Flores/Guatemala
21:10		951	733	Miami/Guatemala
20:19	Continental	1461	72S	Houston/Guatemala
12:00	Copa	110	737	Panamá/San José/Guatemala
20:00		318	737	Panamá/SJO/MGA/SAL/Guate.
08:20	Iberia	6105	D10	Madrid/Miami/Guatemala
16:45	KLM	745	B-747-400	Amsterdam/México/Guatemala
				(Miércoles, viernes y domingo)

Salidas internacionales de Guatemala

Guat.	Compañía	Vuelo	Equipo	Escalas/Rutas
08:15	American	928	757	Guatemala/Miami
13:59		930	72S	Guatemala/Miami
11:20		990	757	Guatemala/Dallas
18:50	Aviateca	960	733	Guatemala/Los Angeles
07:20		961	733	Guatemala/Sal/Managua
17:40		901	733	Guatemala/Managua/San José
07:00		022	73S	Guatemala/Flores
15:00		020	73S	Guatemala/Flores
09:50		910	73S	Guatemala/México
09:00		900	733	Guatemala/Miami
12:30		950	73S	Guatemala/Miami
08:30		920	73S	Guatemala/Mérida/Houston
17:30		930	73S	Guatemala/Flores/Cancún
08:00	Continental	1122	72S	Guatemala/Houston
07:00	Copa	317	737	Guat./Sal/MGA/SJO/Panamá
14:30		111	737	Guatemala/San José/Guatemala
11:10	Iberia	6104	D10	Guatemala/Miami/Madrid
18:45	KLM	746	B-747-400	Guatemala/México/Amsterdam
				(Miércoles, viernes y domingo)

Actividad D Look, listen, and choose.

1. Who is speaking?

    a. the pilot   **b.** the flight attendant   **c.** the airport announcer

2. What is the destination?

    a. North Carolina   **b.** Caracas   **c.** Buenos Aires

3. About how many hours is the flight?

    a. 7   **b.** 9   **c.** 12

4. At what time will they land?

    a. 9:10 A.M.   **b.** 11:00 A.M.   **c.** 12:20 P.M.

5. At what altitude are they?

    a. 1,100 meters   **b.** 11,000 meters   **c.** 111,000 meters

6. What is their air speed?

    a. 120 kph   **b.** 1,200 kph   **c.** 12,000 kph

7. In what direction are they flying?

    a. north   **b.** south   **c.** west

8. What countries will they fly over?

    a. Brazil and Uruguay   **b.** Chile and Bolivia   **c.** Spain and Portugal

9. How many flight attendants are on board?

    a. 12   **b.** 18   **c.** 20

CAPÍTULO 9

DEPORTES Y ACTIVIDADES DE INVIERNO

PRIMERA PARTE

VOCABULARIO

Palabras 1

Actividad A   Listen and repeat.

Actividad B   Listen and choose.

_____   _____   _____

_____   _____   _____

_____   _____

Actividad C   Listen and repeat.

Actividad D   Listen and choose.

1. sí   no   **2.** sí   no   **3.** sí   no   **4.** sí   no   **5.** sí   no

Actividad E   Listen and repeat.

Actividad F   Listen and choose.

1. sí   no   **2.** sí   no   **3.** sí   no   **4.** sí   no

Actividad G   Listen and choose.

1. a   b   c   **3.** a   b   c   **5.** a   b   c

2. a   b   c   **4.** a   b   c   **6.** a   b   c

Palabras 2

Actividad H   Listen and repeat.

Actividad I   Listen and choose.

1. sí   no   2. sí   no   3. sí   no   4. sí   no   5. sí   no

Actividad J   Listen.

Actividad K   Listen and choose.

1. sí   no   2. sí   no   3. sí   no   4. sí   no   5. sí   no

ESTRUCTURA

Actividad A   Listen and choose.

1. saber	conocer	**4.** saber	conocer	**7.** saber	conocer
2. saber	conocer	**5.** saber	conocer	**8.** saber	conocer
3. saber	conocer	**6.** saber	conocer	**9.** saber	conocer

Actividad B   Listen and choose.

1. a   b   c   3. a   b   c   5. a   b   c

2. a   b   c   4. a   b   c

Actividad C   Listen and answer.

Example: (*You hear*)   ¿Qué libro quieres?
            (*You see*)   allí
            (*You say*)   Quiero ese libro.

1. allí   3. allá   5. allá   7. aquí

2. aquí   4. aquí   6. allí   8. allí

CONVERSACIÓN

Actividad D   Listen.

Actividad E   Listen and complete.

1.   Carmen sabe esquiar pero no es _____.

2.   Ella quiere esquiar más pero no _____.

3.   No hay una _____ de esquí cerca de donde ella vive.

4.   Donde ella vive no hay montañas, sólo _____.

5.   Su amigo recomienda el esquí de _____.

PRONUNCIACIÓN

Actividad F   Pronunciación: *La consonante* g

The consonant *g* has two sounds, hard and soft. You will study the soft sound in Chapter 10. *G* in combination with *a, o, u (ga, go, gu)* is pronounced somewhat like the *g* in the English word *go*. To maintain this hard *g* sound with *e* or *i*, a *u* is placed after the *g: gue, gui*. Listen and repeat after the speaker.

SEGUNDA PARTE

Actividad A   Listen and answer.

1.   What is the ad for?

   a. ski trips   **b.** skating lessons   **c.** sportswear

2.   How many days is the stay at the resort?

   a. 4   **b.** 8   **c.** 12

3.   What is the destination?

   a. Buenos Aires   **b.** Córdoba   **c.** Bariloche

4.   How many departures are there per week?

   a. 2   **b.** 4   **c.** 8

5.   What is the means of transportation?

   a. bus   **b.** train   **c.** plane

6. What is the price?

    a. 500 pesos   b. 5,000 pesos   c. 15,000 pesos

7. What is the address of the agency?

    a. Córdoba 81   b. Buenos Aires 80   c. Gorostiza 88

8. What is their phone number?

    a. 312-69-75   b. 312-67-59   c. 312-77-69

Actividad B   Listen and choose.

round-trip air travel   hotel room

all meals   all ski equipment: skis, poles, boots, etc.

unlimited passes to the slopes   bus transportation from the hotel
                                               to the slopes

classes for beginners

Actividad C   Listen and answer.

——— Para viajeros ———

España	M.	m.	S.	España	M.	m.	S.	España	M.	m.	S.	Extran.	M.	m.	S.
Albacete	12	6	Ll	Huelva	16	8	Ll	Palma	18	8	C	Amsterdam .	14	4	C
Algeciras ...	16	12	P	Huesca	13	7	Ll	Pamplona...	8	7	Ll	Atenas	16	12	C
Alicante.....	18	14	Ll	Ibiza	17	11	Ll	Pontevedra .	14	4	P	Berlín	6	-2	D
Almería	17	12	P	Jaén	14	7	Ll	Salamanca..	3	0	N	Bruselas	12	8	C
Avila	4	-1	N	Jerez	16	8	C	S. Sebastián	11	8	Ll	B. Aires	22	8	D
Badajoz	14	7	P	La Coruña ..	14	11	C	Santander ..	11	8	Ll	Copenhague	8	5	D
Barcelona...	20	12	Ll	Lanzarote ...	22	16	P	Santiago	11	4	C	Dublín	11	5	C
Bilbao	11	9	Ll	Las Palmas .	22	17	C	Segovia	3	0	N	Estocolmo ..	7	3	D
Burgos	3	1	Ll	León	9	3	Ll	Sevilla	14	9	P	Francfort....	10	2	D
Cáceres	8	6	C	Lérida	16	8	Ll	Soria	4	3	Ll	Ginebra	7	5	C
Cádiz.......	17	11	C	Logroño	7	6	Ll	Tarragona ..	18	14	Ll	Lisboa	14	9	P
Castellón ...	15	11	Ll	Lugo	12	1	P	Tenerife	23	17	C	Londres	11	8	C
Ceuta	15	12	P	Mahón......	19	11	P	Teruel	9	5	Ll	México	23	8	D
C. Real	7	6	Ll	Málaga	21	12	Ll	Toledo......	12	7	Ll	Milán	10	8	C
Córdoba	10	9	Ll	Melilla	17	13	P	Valencia	17	14	Ll	Moscú ......-10	-13	D
Cuenca.....	10	5	Ll	Murcia......	16	14	P	Valladolid ...	5	1	Ll	Niza........	16	14	D
Gerona	15	12	C	Orense	12	4	P	Vitoria	7	6	Ll	Nueva York .	12	6	C
Granada	14	12	C	Oviedo	11	5	Ll	Zamora	10	7	Ll	París	12	8	P
Guadalajara .	10	6	Ll	Palencia	10	4	P	Zaragoza ...	10	8	Ll	Roma	18	13	C

ABREVIATURAS.–M.: Temperatura máxima.–m.: Temperatura mínima.–S.: Situación ambiental.–D.: Despejado.–C.: Cubierto.–Ll.: Lluvias.–P.: Parcialmente cubierto.–T.: Tormentas.–N.: Nieve.–n.: Niebla.–Ch.: Chubascos.–(Datos del INM.)

Actividad D   Listen and choose.

1.   **a.** prices   **b.** the weather   **c.** hours

2.   **a.** transportation   **b.** facilities   **c.** rooms

3.   **a.** lessons   **b.** the weather   **c.** food

4.   **a.** rooms   **b.** hours   **c.** transportation

5.   **a.** the weather   **b.** prices   **c.** hours

6.   **a.** food   **b.** transportation   **c.** lessons

7.   **a.** rooms   **b.** facilities   **c.** the weather

8.   **a.** facilities   **b.** lessons   **c.** prices

9.   **a.** transportation   **b.** the weather   **c.** hours

CAPÍTULO

10

LA SALUD Y EL MÉDICO

PRIMERA PARTE

VOCABULARIO

Palabras 1

Actividad A   Listen and repeat.

Actividad B   Listen and choose.

_____   _____   _____

_____   _____   _____

Actividad C   Listen and choose.

1. a   b   c   **3.** a   b   c   **5.** a   b   c

2. a   b   c   **4.** a   b   c   **6.** a   b   c

Palabras 2

Actividad D   Listen and repeat.

Actividad E   Listen and choose.

_____   _____   _____

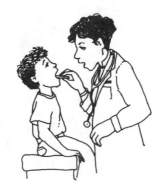

_____   _____   _____

Actividad F   Listen and repeat.

Actividad G   Listen and choose.

1. sí no	**3.** sí no	**5.** sí no
2. sí no	**4.** sí no	**6.** sí no

ESTRUCTURA

Actividad A   Listen and answer.

1. alto, rubio	**4.** sí	**7.** inteligente, simpático(a)
2. simpáticos	**5.** grande, moderna	**8.** interesante
3. no, antipática	**6.** Gonzalo	**9.** difícil

Actividad B   Listen and answer.

1. enfermo

2. bien

3. aburridos

4. cansados

5. triste

6. no, tranquilos

7. contenta

Actividad C   Listen and create.

Example: *(You see)*   el médico / muy bueno
    (You say)   El médico es muy bueno.

1. la médica / inteligente

2. su consulta / moderna

3. el enfermero / muy bueno

4. la muchacha / enferma

5. la consulta / en el edificio Burgos

6. el edificio / alto

7. el paciente / el hospital

8. el hospital / viejo

Actividad D   Listen and choose.

1.	location	origin	4.	location	origin	7.	location	origin
2.	location	origin	5.	location	origin	8.	location	origin
3.	location	origin	6.	location	origin	9.	location	origin

Actividad E   Listen and choose.

1. characteristic condition origin location

2. characteristic condition origin location

3. characteristic condition origin location

4. characteristic condition origin location

5. characteristic condition origin location

6. characteristic condition origin location

7. characteristic condition origin location

8. characteristic condition origin location

9. characteristic condition origin location

Actividad F   Listen and answer.

Example: *(You hear)*   ¿Qué te duele, Margarita?
(You see)   la garganta
(You say)   Me duele la garganta.

1. la enfermera   3. la médica   5. no

2. la cabeza   4. unas pastillas   6. el farmacéutico

CONVERSACIÓN

Actividad G   Listen.

Actividad H   Listen and choose.

1. a   b   3. a   b   5. a   b

2. a   b   4. a   b   6. a   b

PRONUNCIACIÓN

Actividad I   Pronunciación: *La consonante* j

The Spanish *j* sound does not exist in English. In Spain the *j* sound is very guttural (coming from the throat). In Latin America the *j* is much softer. Listen and repeat after the speaker.

G in combination with *e* or *i* (*ge, gi*) has the same sound as the *j*. For this reason you must pay particular attention to the spelling of the words with *je, ji, ge,* and *gi.* Listen and repeat after the speaker.

SEGUNDA PARTE

Actividad A   Listen and choose.

_____ I don't take any medication.   _____ I don't have allergies.

_____ I do aerobic exercises.   _____ What is your diagnosis?

_____ Do I need vitamins?   _____ I consume few calories.

_____ I eat a lot of fiber.   _____ What are my symptoms?

_____ Do I have to go on a diet?

Actividad B   Listen and complete.

Actividad C   Listen and answer.

FARMACIAS

■ MALAGA.
9.30 a 22.00: Gonzalo Lazárraga, Puente Palmilla. M. Carmen Escuder, Camino Suárez 59. Luisa M. Villén, avda. Europa 111. Carlos Pérez, Plaza Merced 9. Matilde Rubio, Montes de Oca 18. Ignacio Muñoz, avda. Sor Tsa. Prat 54. Miguel D. Narváez, avda. Andalucía 61.
22.00 a 9.30: Luis del Río, avda. Paloma 8. M. Teresa Gómez, Diego V. Otero 3. José L. León, Plaza Verdiales 9 bajo 1.

■ ANTEQUERA. Cándido Vidal, Cantareros 24.

■ BENALMADENA.   Antonio G–Guillamón, ctra. Cádiz km. 227 (Maite I).

■ ESTEPONA.   Eloisa García, Adolfo Suárez 2.

■ FUENGIROLA. Rosario Mena, Nuevo Mijas 6, local 3.

■ MARBELLA. Pilar Pérez, avda. Ricardo Soriano edif. Altamira.

■ RINCON DE LA VICTORIA. José Abaurre. Avda. Mediterráneo, 75.

■ RONDA. Serrano, calle Espinel.

■ TORRE DEL MAR. Conchita R. Díaz, calle del Mar 24.

■ TORREMOLINOS. Armando Chocróm, avda. Principal (Playamar).

■ VELEZ MALAGA.   Alfonso Zarza, Lope de Vega 5.

Actividad D   Listen and complete.

1. The ad is for people with _____.

2. The name of the product is _____.

3. It is an _____.

4. It can be obtained in a _____.

5. It comes in the form of _____.

6. It is available in _____ sizes.

ACTIVIDADES DE VERANO

PRIMERA PARTE

VOCABULARIO

Palabras 1

Actividad A   Listen and repeat.

Actividad B   Listen and choose.

Actividad C   Listen and repeat.

Actividad D   Listen and choose.

1. sí no			**4.** sí no			**7.** sí no		
2. sí no			**5.** sí no			**8.** sí no		
3. sí no			**6.** sí no			**9.** sí no		

Actividad E   Listen and choose.

1. a   b   c   **5.** a   b   c

2. a   b   c   **6.** a   b   c

3. a   b   c   **7.** a   b   c

4. a   b   c

Palabras 2

Actividad F   Listen and repeat.

Actividad G   Listen and choose.

 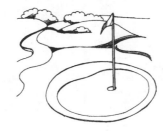 

_____   _____   _____

Actividad H   Listen and choose.

1. sí no	**4.** sí no	**7.** sí no
2. sí no	**5.** sí no	**8.** sí no
3. sí no	**6.** sí no	**9.** sí no

ESTRUCTURA

Actividad A   Listen and answer.

1. la playa	**5.** no
2. 1:00	**6.** sí, Laura
3. sí	**7.** no
4. una toalla y una silla plegable	**8.** 6:00

Actividad B   Listen, answer, and ask.

Example: *(You hear)*   ¿Uds. nadaron?
                 (You say)   Sí, nadamos. Y tú, ¿nadaste?

Actividad C   Listen and ask.

Example: *(You hear)*   Ayer cantamos.
                 (You see)   dónde
                 (You say)   ¿Dónde cantaron Uds.?

1. dónde	**3.** a quiénes	**5.** qué
2. a qué	**4.** dónde	**6.** para qué

Actividad D   Listen and answer.

Example: *(You hear)*   ¿Los anteojos de sol?
                 (You say)   Sí, los tengo.

Actividad E   Listen and answer.

1. a la playa	**3.** Luisa	**5.** en carro
2. no	**4.** a las dos	

Actividad F   Listen and answer.

1. doña Teresa	**3.** los amigos	**5.** tú
2. yo	**4.** nosotros	

CONVERSACIÓN

Actividad G Listen.

Actividad H Listen and choose.

1. sí   no   **3.** sí   no   **5.** sí   no   **7.** sí   no

2. sí   no   **4.** sí   no   **6.** sí   no   **8.** sí   no

PRONUNCIACIÓN

Actividad I Pronunciación: *La consonante* r

The Spanish trilled *r* sound does not exist in English. When a word begins with an *r* (initial position), the *r* is trilled. Within the word, double *r* (*rr*) is also pronounced as a trilled sound. Listen and repeat after the speaker.

The sound for a single *r* within a word (medial position) does not exist in English either. It is trilled less than the initial *r* or *rr*. Listen and repeat after the speaker.

SEGUNDA PARTE

Actividad A Look, listen, and choose.

1.   ¿Para quiénes es el anuncio?

   a. para personas que quieren trabajo   **b.** para enfermos

   c. para personas que van de vacaciones

2.   ¿Cuál es el nombre del lugar que anuncian?

   a. Palmas del Mar   **b.** Vistas de Palma   **c.** San Juan

3.   ¿Dónde está el lugar?

   a. en un lago   **b.** en las montañas   **c.** en la costa

4.   ¿Qué deporte no menciona el anuncio?

   a. el esquí acuático   **b.** el golf   **c.** el tenis

5.   ¿Qué pueden hacer las personas que no quieren hacer deportes?

   a. tomar el sol   **b.** ir a San Juan   **c.** esquiar

6.   ¿A cuántos kilómetros de San Juan está?

   a. cuatro   **b.** catorce   **c.** cuarenta

Actividad B   Look, listen, and write.

1. What kind of product is being advertised?

    _____

2. What is the name of the product?

    _____

3. Where should you take it?

    _____

4. What will it do for you?

    _____

5. How much does it cost?

    _____

Actividad C   Listen and complete.

1. The reporter is in the town of _____.

2. This town is in the area or region of _____.

3. In Castilla la Mancha there are over 80 _____.

4. They are suitable for the following activities: _____.

5. They are also excellent for fishing when there is _____.

6. Some of them have fresh water and others have salt

    _____.

7. They contain mud that is supposed to be good for a number of

    _____.

8. Some of them are _____ and

    _____.

9. Many of these lagoons are excellent for _____ and
    foreign tourism.

10. They are usually very _____, something that is hard to
    find today.

CAPÍTULO
12

ACTIVIDADES CULTURALES

PRIMERA PARTE

VOCABULARIO

Palabras 1

Actividad A Listen and repeat.

Actividad B Listen and choose.

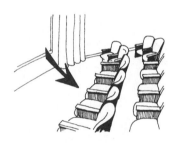

_____

_____

_____

_____

_____

_____

Actividad C Listen and repeat.

Actividad D Listen and choose.

1. a   b   c   4. a   b   c

2. a   b   c   5. a   b   c

3. a   b   c

Actividad E   Listen and choose.

1. **a.** en la pantalla   **b.** en la butaca   **c.** en la taquilla

2. **a.** entradas   **b.** butacas   **c.** películas

3. **a.** taquillas   **b.** películas   **c.** filas

4. **a.** butacas   **b.** pantallas   **c.** entradas

5. **a.** una entrada   **b.** una fila   **c.** una taquilla

6. **a.** en una pantalla   **b.** en una butaca   **c.** en una entrada

Actividad F   Listen and choose.

1. sí   no   3. sí   no   5. sí   no   7. sí   no

2. sí   no   4. sí   no   6. sí   no   8. sí   no

Actividad G   Listen and repeat.

Actividad H   Listen and choose.

1. **a.** en el cine   **b.** en el museo   **c.** en el mural

2. **a.** estatuas   **b.** escultores   **c.** artistas

3. **a.** músicos   **b.** escultores   **c.** turistas

4. **a.** un cuadro   **b.** un museo   **c.** un artista

5. **a.** una escultura   **b.** una exposición   **c.** un mural

6. **a.** al cine   **b.** al concierto   **c.** a una exposición de arte

7. **a.** al turista   **b.** a la orquesta   **c.** al director de orquesta

Palabras 2

Actividad I   Listen and repeat.

Actividad J   Listen and choose.

1. **a.** un actor   **b.** un artista   **c.** un telón

2. **a.** una estatua   **b.** una butaca   **c.** una actriz

3. **a.** el actor   **b.** el teatro   **c.** el telón

4. **a.** el mesero   **b.** la mesa   **c.** el público

5. **a.** la propina   **b.** la cuenta   **c.** el menú

6. **a.** la propina   **b.** la cuenta   **c.** el menú

Actividad K   Listen and choose.

1.	sí	no	**3.**	sí	no	**5.**	sí	no
2.	sí	no	**4.**	sí	no	**6.**	sí	no

Actividad L   Listen and choose.

1.	a	b	c	**4.**	a	b	c	**7.**	a	b	c
2.	a	b	c	**5.**	a	b	c	**8.**	a	b	c
3.	a	b	c	**6.**	a	b	c	**9.**	a	b	c

ESTRUCTURA

Actividad A   Listen and answer.

1.	cine	**5.**	en un restaurante
2.	película nueva	**6.**	un menú
3.	documental	**7.**	a Josefina
4.	9:00	**8.**	11:00

Actividad B   Listen and answer.

1.	sí	**3.**	sí	**5.**	no, hablar
2.	las noticias	**4.**	sí		

Actividad C   Listen and answer.

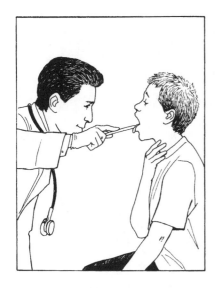
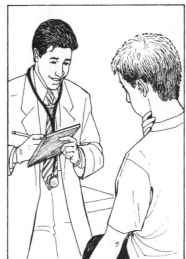
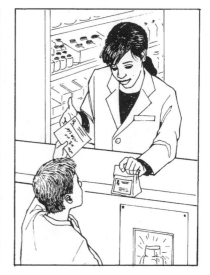

CONVERSACIÓN

Actividad D   Listen.

Actividad E   Listen and choose.

1. sí   no   3. sí   no   5. sí   no

2. sí   no   4. sí   no   6. sí   no

PRONUNCIACIÓN

Actividad F   Pronunciación: *La* h, *la* y, *la* ll

The *h* in Spanish is silent. It is never pronounced. Listen and repeat after the speaker.

Y in Spanish can be either a vowel or a consonant. As a vowel it is pronounced exactly the same as the vowel *i*. Listen and repeat after the speaker.

Y is a consonant when it begins a word or a syllable. As a consonant, *y* is pronounced similarly to the English *y* in the word *yoyo*. This sound has several variations throughout the Spanish-speaking world. Listen and repeat after the speaker.

Until 1994, the *ll* was considered a single consonant in Spanish and was a separate letter of the alphabet. In many areas of the Spanish-speaking world it is pronounced the same as the *y*. It too has several variations. Listen and repeat after the speaker.

SEGUNDA PARTE

Actividad A   Listen and write.

1. _____

2. _____

3. _____

4. _____

5. _____

6. _____

7. _____

8. _____

9. _____

Actividad B Listen and write.

1. What kind of radio broadcast is it?

   _____

2. When was the first performance?

   _____

3. What is the title?

   _____

4. Who is Guillermo Sampere?

   _____

5. What happened to Angelito?

   _____

6. Whom did the parents call?

   _____

7. Where was Angelito found?

   _____

8. Who is Conrado Herrero?

   _____

9. Who is Sandra Arniches?

   _____

10. Where can you see the film?

   _____

11. What is the location of the theater?

   _____

12. What would seem to be a convenient way to get there?

   _____

13. How many shows a day are there?

   _____

Actividad C   Look, listen, and write.

Venta EL ORO

JUANA CANO GUERRERO · D.N.I. 31.954.412

Bar-Restaurante

Carretera Cádiz-Málaga Km. 115 - Tel. 66 47 72

GUADACORTE
(Los Barrios)   6- 8- 94

Mesa Núm. _15_   **Factura Núm.** _1646_

		PESETAS
	Ensalada	250
1	Queso E.	500
1	Pargo Espalda 450 gro.	1350
1	Rabo.	700
1	B. Vino.	350
1/2	Mineral.	60
	pan	80
	Cafes y Copas	350
		3.640

I.V.A. INCLUIDO (Tipo aplicado 6 %)   TOTAL...

1. _____   7. _____

2. _____   8. _____

3. _____   9. _____

4. _____   10. _____

5. _____   11. _____

6. _____   12. _____

Actividad D   Look, listen, and answer.

¿Dónde está nuestro hijo?

Director   Guillermo Sampere

Actores   Sandra Arniches / Conrado Herrera

Sesiones   martes y miércoles   8:00 P.M.
jueves   2:00 P.M. y 8:00 P.M.
sábado   3:00 P.M. y 9:00 P.M.
domingo   2:00 P.M. y 8:00 P.M.
lunes   descanso, no hay función

¡NO HAY ENTRADAS PARA ESTE SÁBADO!

Precios   Butacas de patio, filas 1–11   500 pesos
Butacas de patio, filas 12–26   300 pesos
Balcones   150 pesos

CAPÍTULO

13

LA ROPY Y LA MODA

PRIMERA PARTE

VOCABULARIO

Palabras 1

Actividad A   Listen and repeat.

Actividad B   Listen and choose.

_____   _____   _____

_____   _____   _____

_____   _____   _____

Actividad C   Listen and repeat.

Actividad D   Listen and choose.

1. sí no		**3.** sí no		**5.** sí no		**7.** sí no	
2. sí no		**4.** sí no		**6.** sí no		**8.** sí no	

Actividad E   Listen and choose.

1. a b c	**3.** a b c	**5.** a b c	**7.** a b c
2. a b c	**4.** a b c	**6.** a b c	**8.** a b c

Palabras 2

Actividad F   Listen and repeat.

Actividad G   Listen and choose.

_____ _____ _____

_____ _____ _____

Actividad H   Listen and repeat.

Actividad I   Listen and choose.

1. sí   no   2. sí   no   3. sí   no   4. sí   no   5. sí   no

ESTRUCTURA

Actividad A   Listen and answer.

1. la historia   3. el fútbol   5. no, qué

2. la geografía   4. el cine

Actividad B   Listen and answer.

Actividad C   Listen and answer.

1. a mi amigo   3. a las muchachas   5. el baloncesto

2. no   4. no, patinar   6. las piscinas

Actividad D   Listen and answer.

gustar   encantar   aburrir   interesar

Actividad E   Listen and answer.

Actividad F   Listen and answer.

CONVERSACIÓN

Actividad G   Listen.

Actividad H   Listen and choose.

1. sí   no   4. sí   no   7. sí   no

2. sí   no   5. sí   no   8. sí   no

3. sí   no   6. sí   no   9. sí   no

PRONUNCIACIÓN

Actividad I   Pronunciación: *Las consonantes* ñ y ch

The *ñ* is a separate letter of the Spanish alphabet. The mark over it is called a *tilde*. Note that it is pronounced similarly to the *ny* in the English word *canyon*. Listen and repeat after the speaker.

Until 1994, the *ch* was considered a separate letter of the Spanish alphabet. It is pronounced much like the *ch* in the English word *church*. Listen and repeat after the speaker.

SEGUNDA PARTE

Actividad A Listen and choose.

1. sí   no   **2.** sí   no   **3.** sí   no   **4.** sí   no   **5.** sí   no

Actividad B Listen and choose.

1. **a.** una blusa   **b.** zapatos   **c.** pantalones
2. **a.** una camisa   **b.** un abrigo   **c.** un sombrero
3. **a.** sandalias   **b.** una falda   **c.** una corbata
4. **a.** un cinturón   **b.** un vestido   **c.** zapatos
5. **a.** una blusa   **b.** calcetines   **c.** un abrigo
6. **a.** tenis   **b.** medias   **c.** sandalias
7. **a.** un saco   **b.** un suéter   **c.** un sombrero
8. **a.** el traje   **b.** la camisa   **c.** el suéter
9. **a.** las camisetas   **b.** las sandalias   **c.** las medias

Actividad C Listen and answer.

Actividad D Listen and answer.

EN
SORIANA

Para Damas

30%
DE DESCUENTO
EN LAS
•PANTIMEDIAS
DE LICRA, DE LA MARCA "SPANEL"
EN LOS
•PANTALONES
DE LA MARCA "SANTORY" Y "LODY"

ADEMAS:
MUCHAS OFERTAS
INTERNAS
EN TODOS NUESTROS DEPARTAMENTOS.

Para Niñas

30%
DE DESCUENTO
EN TODAS LAS
•BLUSAS
EN TODAS LAS
•PANTALETAS

Para Caballeros

30%
DE DESCUENTO
EN TODAS LAS
•CAMISAS
SPORT
EN LOS
PANTALONES
DE MEZCLILLA.
EN LAS
PLAYERAS.
EN LA
•ROPA INTERIOR
DE LA MARCA "TEYCON"

Para Niños

BERMUDA
100% ALG. ESTAMPADO Y LISO, VARIOS COLORES, T. 6-16, DE LA MARCA "MARK ELIOT", DE N$ 16.90
A SOLO N $ **8.45**

TRUZA
100% POLY., VARIOS COLORES Y ESTAMPADOS, T. 4-16, DE LA MARCA "ELEGANZA", DE N$ 4.50
A SOLO N $ **2.25**

CAMISA
SPORT MANGA CORTA, 100% ALG. VARIOS ESTAMPADOS Y COLORES, T. 4-16, DE LA MARCA "MASH SPORT", DE N$ 29.90
A SOLO N $ **14.95**

PANTALON
JUVENIL CON PLIEGUES, EN POLY./ALG. VARIOS COLORES, T. 6-16, DE LA MARCA "REGENT", DE N$ 32.90
A SOLO N $ **16.45**

CAPÍTULO

14

UN VIAJE EN TREN

PRIMERA PARTE

VOCABULARIO

Palabras 1

Actividad A   Listen and repeat.

Actividad B   Listen and choose.

_____   _____   _____

_____   _____   _____

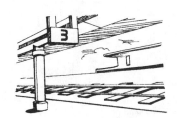

_____   _____   _____

Actividad C Listen and choose.

1. sí   no   3. sí   no   5. sí   no

2. sí   no   4. sí   no   6. sí   no

Actividad D Listen and choose.

1. a   b   c   4. a   b   c   7. a   b   c

2. a   b   c   5. a   b   c   8. a   b   c

3. a   b   c   6. a   b   c   9. a   b   c

Palabras 2

Actividad E Listen and repeat.

Actividad F Listen and choose.

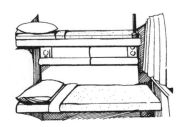

STUDENT TAPE MANUAL

Actividad G Listen and choose.

1. sí   no   4. sí   no   7. sí   no
2. sí   no   5. sí   no   8. sí   no
3. sí   no   6. sí   no   9. sí   no

ESTRUCTURA

Actividad A Listen and choose.

1. a   b   c   4. a   b   c
2. a   b   c   5. a   b   c
3. a   b   c   6. a   b   c

Actividad B Listen and answer.

1. a las siete   5. Emilio
2. a las cinco   6. en segunda
3. en tren   7. sí
4. el rápido

Actividad C Listen and choose.

1. a   b   c   3. a   b   c   5. a   b   c
2. a   b   c   4. a   b   c   6. a   b   c

CONVERSACIÓN

Actividad D Listen.

Actividad E Listen and choose.

1. sí   no   6. sí   no
2. sí   no   7. sí   no
3. sí   no   8. sí   no
4. sí   no   9. sí   no
5. sí   no   10. sí   no

PRONUNCIACIÓN

Actividad F Pronunciación: *La consonante* x

An *x* between two vowels is pronounced much like the English *x* but a bit softer. Listen and repeat after the speaker.

When *x* is followed by a consonant, it is often pronounced like an *s*. Listen and repeat after the speaker.

SEGUNDA PARTE

Actividad A Listen and write.

	hora	destino	andén
1.	_____	_____	_____
2.	_____	_____	_____
3.	_____	_____	_____
4.	_____	_____	_____
5.	_____	_____	_____

Actividad B Listen and answer.

RENFE

TREN	TARIFA	IMPORTE	CLASE
200 / 1		1.200	2

MADRID
CHAMARTIN

NO ES VALIDO SIN IMPRESION DE MAQUINA.
ENTREGUESE A LA LLEGADA. INCLUIDO S.O.V.

FECHA   **BILLETE N.°**
21OCT94 6588

Actividad C   Listen and write.

1. Where is this conversation probably taking place?

   _____

2. What kind of ticket does Gerardo have?

   _____

3. When does Gerardo plan to return?

   _____

4. How much is a one-way ticket?

   _____

5. How much is a round-trip ticket?

   _____

6. What is the young woman suggesting?

   _____

CAPÍTULO

15

EN EL RESTAURANTE

PRIMERA PARTE

VOCABULARIO

Palabras 1

Actividad A Listen and repeat.

Actividad B Listen and choose.

1. sí	no	**4.** sí	no	**7.** sí	no
2. sí	no	**5.** sí	no	**8.** sí	no
3. sí	no	**6.** sí	no	**9.** sí	no

Actividad C Listen and choose.

1. a	b	c	**5.** a	b	c
2. a	b	c	**6.** a	b	c
3. a	b	c	**7.** a	b	c
4. a	b	c			

Actividad D   Listen and choose.

_____   _____   _____

_____   _____   _____

Palabras 2

Actividad E   Listen and repeat.

Actividad F   Listen and choose.

_____   _____   _____

_____   _____   _____

Actividad G   Listen and answer.

1.

2.

3.

4.

5.

6.

7.

8.

9.

ESTRUCTURA

Actividad A   Listen and choose.

1.	a	b	c	**4.**	a	b	c	**7.**	a	b	c
2.	a	b	c	**5.**	a	b	c	**8.**	a	b	c
3.	a	b	c	**6.**	a	b	c	**9.**	a	b	c

Actividad B   Listen and answer.

1.

2.

3.

4.

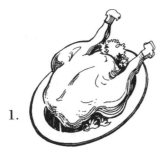

5.

6.

7.

8.

9.

CONVERSACIÓN

Actividad C   Listen.

Actividad D   Listen and choose.

1. sí no		**3.** sí no		**5.** sí no		**7.** sí no
2. sí no		**4.** sí no		**6.** sí no		**8.** sí no

PRONUNCIACIÓN

Actividad E   Pronunciación: *La acentuación*

The rules of stress or accentuation in Spanish are simple. Words ending in a vowel, *n,* or *s* are accented on the next-to-last syllable. Listen and repeat after the speaker.

Words ending in a consonant (except *n* or *s*) are accented on the last syllable. Listen and repeat after the speaker.

Words that do not follow the above rules must have a written accent mark over the stressed syllable. Listen and repeat after the speaker.

A word of one syllable (monosyllabic) does not take an accent unless the same word can have two different meanings. The written accent mark distinguishes between words that are spelled alike but have different meanings. Listen and repeat after the speaker.

SEGUNDA PARTE

Actividad A   Listen and choose.

1.   ¿De qué trata el anuncio?

    a. del sol   **b.** de un viaje   **c.** de un restaurante

2.   ¿Dónde está el Sol?

    a. en Cuba   **b.** en el centro de la ciudad   **c.** en todos los países hispanos

3.   ¿Qué tipo de comida sirven?

    a. solamente comida hispana   **b.** solamente comida cubana

    c. solamente comida mexicana

4.   ¿Cuál es la especialidad los martes?

    a. masitas de cerdo a la cubana   **b.** paella valenciana

    c. enchiladas de México

5.   ¿Qué se puede hacer por teléfono?

    a. reservaciones   **b.** paella   **c.** pagar

Actividad B   Look, listen, and write.

Salón Monserrate

Hotel Tequendama

Al almuerzo, variado buffet ejecutivo diferente cada día de la semana. Para cenar, una rica carta de platos internacionales, estupendo servicio de bar, alegría con la orquesta de plata y permanentes shows.

Los Arcos

Hotel La Fontana

Sobre el apacible patio de ladrillos y geranios del hotel La Fontana en un ambiente tropical y elegante, funciona el restaurante Los Arcos. Allí se está dando gran impulso a la "Nueva Cocina Colombiana". Se han inventado platos exquisitos logrando finas y novedosas combinaciones con productos autóctonos
Lunes a Domingo, 7p.m. - 12p.m.

La Biblioteca

Hotel Charleston

El restaurante la Biblioteca en el lobby del hotel Charleston es uno de los más exclusivos y concurridos de Bogotá, sitio ideal para comida en calma, rodeada de lucidez y sabiduría, o para un agradable desayuno de trabajo.
A través de festivales gastronómicos anuales se ha ido formando una carta especializada y exquisita.
Lunes a Domingo, 6a.m. - 12 m.

El Virrey

Siempre informal, mantiene sus puertas abiertas todo el día para desayunar, almorzar, tomar el té y cenar a la manera criolla o internacional.

LaCascada

Paraiso de la cocina italiana en un cálido ambiente amenizado por un pianista y el relajante sonido de la cascada.

1. _____

2. _____

3. _____

4. _____

Actividad C Look, listen, and answer.

R E S T A U R A N T E S

COMO MANEJAR EL LISTADO

● El horario al público de los restaurantes es en la mayoría de los casos de 12,30 a 16 horas y de 20 a 24 horas. En caso contrario se especificará el horario oportunamente.

● Para realizar el listado por orden alfabético se han desechado los artículos.

● El precio medio es indicativo y facilitado por el propio restaurante.

● Cuando no se especifica algún día de cierre significa que el restaurante permanece abierto todos los días de la semana.

A

☐ **A'ASQUIÑIÑA.**
Modesto Lafuente, 88. Cocina gallega. Especialidad en mariscos y pescados. Domingo noche, cerrado. Admite tarjetas. Precio medio, de 2.000 a 3.000 pesetas.

☐ **A RODA DE XAN.**
Doctor Esquerdo, 70. Tel. 274 18 22. Cocina gallega. Especialidad en mariscos y pulpo. Admite tarjetas. Precio medio, de 3.000 a 4.000 pesetas.

☐ **¡A TODO MEXICO!**
San Bernardino, 4. Tel. 541 93 59. Plaza República del Ecuador, 4. Tel. 259 48 33. San Leonardo, 3. Tel. 247 54 39. Cocina mexicana. Especialidad en tamales, mole poblado y carnitas. Admite tarjetas. Precio medio, de 1.000 a 2.000 pesetas.

☐

La abaoesa

Huertas, 43 Tel. 429 80 63. Especialidad en carnes rojas a la parrilla de carbón y merluza. Cerrado sábados a mediodía y domingos. Precio medio, de 3.000 a 4.000 pesetas. Reservas.

☐ **ABACO.**
Jovellanos, 6 (junto al teatro de la Zarzuela). Tel. 429 78 68. Abierto de 11 de la mañana a 1 de la madrugada. Viernes y sábados, hasta las 3 de la madrugada. Coctelería internacional.

☐ **LA ABUELITA**
Avenida de Badajoz, 25 (Arturo Soria). Tel. 405 49 94. Especialidad en hojaldre de cabrales, bacalao mujelina de ajos y puding especial de chocolate. Domingos y agosto, cerrado. Admite tarjetas. Precio medio de 3.000 pesetas.

☐ **ACTOR'S.**
Basílica, 17. Tel. 455 91 65. América interpreta el sabor italiano. Especialidad en pizzas, pasta y ensaladas.

☐ **ADRISH.**
Plaza Conde Toreno, 2 (detrás de la plaza de España). Cocina hindú. Lunes, cerrado. Admite tarjetas. Precio medio, de 1.500 a 2.000 pesetas.

☐ **AIRIÑOS DO MAR.**
Orense, 39. Tel. 456 00 52. Marisquería. Especialidad en mariscos y pescados. Domingos, cerrado. Admite tarjetas.

☐ **ALDABA.**
Alberto Alcocer, 5. Tel. 457 21 93. Cocina vasco-francesa. Especialidad en merluza bermeana. Sábados mediodía y domingos, cerrado. Admite tarjetas. Precio medio, de 3.000 a 4.000 pesetas.

☐ **ALDAR**
Alberto Alcocer, 27. Tel. 259 68 75. Cocina marroquí. Especialidad en cuscús. Domingos tarde, cerrado. Admite tarjetas. Precio medio, de 3.000 a 3.500 pesetas.

☐ **ALJABA.**
Padre Damián, 38. Tel. 457 36 42-250 52 14. Especialidades: pimientos del piquillo rellenos, pescados a la sal, lenguado relleno de salmón y carnes y pescados a la brasa. Admite tarjetas. Precio medio, 3.000 pesetas.

☐ **ALKALA.**
Valenzuela, 9. Tel. 532 45 09. Cocina internacional. Sábados mediodía y domingos, cerrado. Admite tarjetas. Precio medio, de 2.000 a 3.000 pesetas.

☐ **ALKALDE.**
Jorge Juan, 10. Tel. 276 33 59. Cocina vasca. Especialidad en zarcarrón. Admite tarjetas. Precio medio, de 2.000 a 3.000 pesetas.

☐ **AL-MOUNIA.**
Recoletos, 5. Tel. 275 01 73. Cocina árabe. Especialidades en tallín, pinchos morunos y cordero asado. Domingo y lunes, cerrado. Admite tarjetas. Precio medio, de 4.000 a 5.000 pesetas.

☐ **EL ALUBION.**
Urbanización Cuesta Blanca. carretera de Burgos, km. 8,500. Tel. 653 08 78. Cocina casera. Especialidad en alubia roja y merluza a los puerros. Domingos noche, cerrado. Admite tarjetas. Precio medio, de 2.500 a 3.000 pesetas.

☐ **AMALUR.**
Padre Damián, 37. Tel. 457 62 98. Cocina vasca. Especialidad en lubina en salsa de langosta, merluza frita con pimientos y solomillo. D. Pedro. Sábados mediodía y domingos, cerrado. Cenas ambientadas con piano. Admite tarjetas. Precio medio, de 3.500 a 4.500 pesetas.

☐ **AMARILLO OLIVAR.**
Olivar, 22. Tel. 228 15 11. Cocina de ayer, hoy y siempre. Especialidades en morteruelo, hojaldre de puerros y alburuna. Precio medio, de 1.000 a 1.500 pesetas. Sábados y domingos mediodía, menú a 750 pesetas.

☐ **AMAYA.**
General Martínez Campos, 11. Tel. 448 69 18. Cocina casera. Especialidad en sopas de ajo. Abierto hasta la 1,30 de la madrugada. Agosto, cerrado. Precio medio, 1.000 pesetas.

☐ **EL AMPARO.**
Callejón de Puigcerdá, 8. Tel. 431 64 56. Cocina vasco-francesa. Especialidad en hojaldre de mollejas. Sábados mediodía, domingos, festivos y puentes cerrado. Admite tarjetas. Precio medio, superior a 4.000 pesetas. Dos estrellas Michelín.

☐ **AMPOR.**
Pico de Almanzor, 2, polígono industrial Los Linares (Fuenlabrada). Cocina tradicional, carta y autoservicio. Domingos noche, cerrado. Admite tarjetas.

☐ **ANAHI.**
Morería, 11. Tel. 265 12 14. Especialidad en parrilla o comida criolla. Abierto hasta las 3 de la madrugada. Sábados y domingos, mediodía. Lunes, cerrado. Precio medio, 1.200 pesetas.

☐ **ANNAPURNA.**
Zurbano, 5. Tel. 410 77 27. Cocina india. Especialidad en horno tandoor. Domingos y festivos, cerrado. Admite tarjetas.

☐ **ANCORA.**
Orense, 6. Entreplanta. Tel. 456 70 79. Cocina gallega. Especialidad en carnes y pescados. Domingos, cerrado. Precio medio, de 2.000 a 2.500 pesetas.

☐ **ANSORENA.**
Capitán Haya, 55. Tel. 279 64 51. Asador. Especialidad en chuletón de buey. Domingos, cerrado. Admite tarjetas. Precio medio, de 2.000 a 3.000 pesetas.

☐ **APRIORI.**
Argensola, 7. Tel. 410 36 71. Cocina francesa. Sábados mediodía, domin-

Actividad D Look, listen, and answer.

DESAYUNO

PARA EMPEZAR

Jugos fríos

Una mezcla de café regional
Té y leche

Aperitivo de frutas frescas de temporada

PLATOS PRINCIPALES

TORTILLA DE TOMATE Y ESCALONIAS
Una tortilla rellena con tomates y escalonias,
ofrecida con un filete para el desayuno y papas

•

PANCAKES DE BANANA Y NUECES
Acompañados con miel de arce,
servidos con lomo de cerdo ahumado y brocheta de fruta fresca

CANASTILLA DE PAN

Panecillos surtidos
Mermeladas y mantequilla

MERIENDA

PLATO DE FRUTA Y QUESO
Un surtido de quesos finos,
acompañados con fruta fresca de temporada

•

SALTEÑAS DE CARNE DE RES
Una especialidad local, empanada horneada
con relleno de papas y carne de res

Torta de chocolate al estilo tradicional

Actividad E Look, listen, and answer.

TABERNA DE ANTONIO SANCHEZ

MESON DE PAREDES, 13
TELEF. 239 78 26
28012 MADRID

CASA FUNDADA EN 1830
RESTAURANTE

FECHA 18/8/94   MESA 9

CANTIDAD		IMPORTE
3	Pan	150
1	Pisto	400
2	Ael ju	800
1	Callos	550
1	Merluza	990
1	Bacalao	700
1	Trasca	250
3	Caf	180

CAMANDU, S. A. - N.I.F. A 78-011442

Sistemas de Control

SUMA 4020
I.V.A. 6 % . 241

01800   TOTAL 4261

Nombre _____ Fecha _____

CAPÍTULO
16

EL CAMPING

PRIMERA PARTE

VOCABULARIO

Palabras 1

    Actividad A   Listen and repeat.

    Actividad B   Listen and choose.

_____

_____

_____

_____

_____

_____

_____

_____

_____

Actividad C Listen and choose.

1. sí   no   4. sí   no   7. sí   no

2. sí   no   5. sí   no   8. sí   no

3. sí   no   6. sí   no   9. sí   no

Palabras 2

Actividad D Listen and repeat.

Actividad E Listen and choose.

_____   _____   _____

_____   _____   _____

_____   _____   _____

Actividad F   Listen and choose.

1. a	b	c	**5.** a	b	c	**9.** a	b	c
2. a	b	c	**6.** a	b	c	**10.** a	b	c
3. a	b	c	**7.** a	b	c	**11.** a	b	c
4. a	b	c	**8.** a	b	c			

ESTRUCTURA

Actividad A   Listen and answer.

Example: (*You hear*)   ¿Qué hace Marta?
            (*You see*)   lavarse
            (*You say*)   Marta se lava.

Example: (*You hear*)   ¿Qué hace Marta?
            (*You see*)   lavar / carro
            (*You say*)   Marta lava el carro.

1. bañarse   5. lavar / bebé

2. desayunarse   6. mirar / el lago

3. peinarse   7. mirarse / espejo

4. despertar / padres

Actividad B   Listen and answer.

Actividad C   Listen and answer.

Example: (*You hear*)   Ellos se divierten mucho.
            (*You say*)   Nosotros nos divertimos mucho también.

Actividad D   Listen and answer.

Example: (*You hear*)   Ella no se despierta temprano.
            (*You say*)   Yo no me despierto temprano tampoco.

Actividad E   Listen and answer.

Example: (*You hear*)   Ella se acuesta temprano.
            (*You say*)   Ella se acostó temprano anoche también.

CONVERSACIÓN

Actividad F   Listen.

Actividad G   Listen and choose.

   1. sí   no   **2.** sí   no   **3.** sí   no   **4.** sí   no   **5.** sí   no

PRONUNCIACIÓN

Actividad H Pronunciación: *Los diptongos*

The vowels *a, e,* and *o* are considered strong vowels in Spanish; *u* and *i* (and *y*) are weak vowels. When two strong vowels occur together, they are pronounced separately as two syllables. Listen and repeat after the speaker.

When two weak vowels or one weak and one strong vowel occur together, they blend together and are pronounced as one syllable. These are called diphthongs. Listen and repeat after the speaker.

SEGUNDA PARTE

Actividad A Listen and choose.

_____ _____ _____

_____ _____ _____

_____ _____ _____

Actividad B Look, listen, and answer.

1²⁹

SHAMPOO PARA EL BEBE

Walgreens. No irrita los ojos. Botella de 16 oz. Cantidad 144 por farmacia, 2 por cliente. Reg. 2.99

1⁹⁹

BEACHCOMBER

Sandalias de goma. Varios tamaños. Ideal para la playa. Cantidad 48 por farmacia, 2 por cliente. Reg. 2.79

3⁹⁹

BUFFERIN

Alivia el dolor. Sin aspirina. Envase de 100. Pqte. bono con desodorante Ban GRATIS. Cantidad 72 por farmacia, 2 por cliente. Reg. 4.99 pqte.

1²⁹

ACEITE PARA BEBE

Walgreens. Botella de 16 oz. Cantidad 160 por farmacia, 2 por cliente. Reg. 2.99

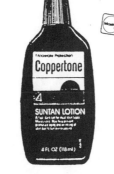

2⁶⁹ COPPERTONE

Loción bronceadora. No. SPF4, para protección. De 4 oz. Cantidad 96 por farmacia, 2 por cliente. Reg. 3.99

4/99[¢] JABON

Walgreens. Gold o Blue Marbleized. Barras de 5 oz. Cantidad 144 por farmacia, 8 por cliente. Reg. 39¢ c/u

1⁴⁹

TALCO PARA BEBE

Walgreens. Protege contra irritación del pañal. Envase de 24 oz. Cantidad 48 por farmacia, 2 por cliente. Reg. 2.99

1⁴⁹

NO-ASPIRIN

Walgreens. Gotas para niños. Alivia fiebre y dolor. Sabor a fruta. Sin alcohol. Con gotero. Frasco de 1/2 oz. Cantidad 36 por farmacia, 2 por cliente. Reg. 1.99

NOTES

NOTES

NOTES

NOTES